# DAFFODILS
# ARE
# DANGEROUS

*The Poisonous Plants*
*in Your Garden*

# Other Books by Hubert Creekmore

*Novels:*  The Fingers of Night
The Welcome
The Chain in the Heart

*Poetry:*  Personal Sun
The Stone Ants
Formula
The Long Reprieve

*Anthologies:*  A Little Treasury of World Poetry
Lyrics of the Middle Ages

*Translations:* The Satires of Juvenal

# DAFFODILS
# ARE
# DANGEROUS

*The Poisonous Plants in Your Garden*

*Hubert Creekmore*

*Illustrations by Helen Spence*

*Walker and Company* ✵ *New York*

Permission to quote the extract on pages 60–61 from Mary Webb's *Precious Bane* by courtesy of E. P. Dutton & Co., Inc.

The lines on page 80 from *The Metamorphoses* by Ovid, translated by Horace Gregory. Copyright © 1958 by the Viking Press, Inc. Reprinted by permission of The Viking Press, Inc.

The lines on page 160 from *The Odyssey* as translated by Robert Fitzgerald. Copyright © 1961 by Robert Fitzgerald. Reprinted by permission of Doubleday & Company, Inc.

# Contents

## THE INDOOR GARDEN                     *227*

Yellow jessamine, Jerusalem cherry, crown of
thorns, candelabra cactus, pencil tree, croton,
*Dieffenbachia*, Chinese evergreen, *Monstera,
Anthurium*, spathe flower, *Philodendron*, pothos,
cyclamen, night-blooming cereus, moonflower
vine, lantana, *Nerine* lily, *Crinum* lily, blood lily,
poinsettia, holly, mistletoe.    *227*

## MISCELLANY                           *244*

Four-o'clock, calycanthus, wisteria, poinciana
tree, sweet pea, lupine, precatory bean, matrimony vine, honeysuckle, woodbine, clematis,
*Vinca*, moonseed, burning bush, mock orange,
hydrangea, snowball bush, elephant's-ear.    *244*

## BIBLIOGRAPHY                         *256*

# Introduction

*Loathsome canker lives in the sweetest bud.—Shakespeare*

I

It's a beautiful garden. The whole family enjoys its color, its aura of rest and quiet and coolness. Against the house is a foundation planting of mountain laurel and rhododendron rolling down to a low border of Japanese yew along whose edges clumps of star-of-Bethlehem and pasque flower peep out and, in season, autumn crocuses. English ivy climbs the enclosing brick walls against which tall spears of delphinium, foxglove and monkshood brace, supported in front by lower bushes of daphne, snow-on-the-mountain, larkspur, bleeding heart and Christmas rose. There are patches of delicate wild blue iris, daffodils and lily of the valley—and a low edging of trimmed box. In one corner is a tall dramatic castor-bean plant to fill in until the cherry laurel grows larger. It's lovely. And every plant in it is poisonous.

The violence of the poisons ranges from comparatively mild—nausea, vomiting, dizziness, diarrhea, prostration—to lethal. The poisonous substances may be in the whole plant or only in one part, such as the root or the seeds. The grown-ups of the family, however, would hardly think of eating a leaf, a seed, or a berry produced in their flower garden. But when the children are in the garden, only casually supervised, the baby may reach from the playpen, or crawl from a blanket, to grasp a berry and eat it. It is a commonplace that the very young put into their mouths any new, bright, attractive object that comes to their hands. Nicander, a Greek physician of the second century B.C., had observed this even in his day and he gave a good physical reason for it—teething. An older child may experiment, out of the natural curiosity of the young, with tasting leaves or berries or, as often happens, may consume a large quantity on a dare from a playmate. Flights of fancy? Only insofar as the fact that the family's children are still alive and well.

It was no flight of fancy that eight children on a springtime frolic along a river bank found what they thought were wild parsnips and in fun ate the roots, as one always wants to eat wild fruits for their distinctive flavors. But the root was the water hemlock plant and the children's death agonies were horrible. And it was no flight of fancy that thirty-two boys of the Brooklyn Orphan Asylum almost died after eating, perhaps in imitation of their elders' tobacco chewing, the newly stripped-off bark of black locust trees that were being prepared as posts to fence in the yard. Children have been poisoned by sucking the nectar from the fragrant blossoms of the yellow jessamine—just as bees and their honey have been. They have been killed by eating daphne berries, the bulbs of star-of-Bethlehem, the red leaves of poinsettia, the nuts of horse chestnut trees and many other plants.

The number of plants that may poison, but without fatal results, is too large to allow treatment of them in this volume, which deals only with those that might be planted in the ordinary flower garden and with those wild plants that may invade the garden. For centuries people

have used these dangerous plants to ornament their dooryards and parks. How then does it happen that they have
not been made ill or killed in numbers large enough to
have caused these plants to be shunned long ago? The
answer lies in habit and ignorance—the fact that many
have suffered from the plants in the past and still are doing
so, without knowing the cause. Ordinarily we eat plants
not from our flower garden but from our vegetable garden,
*i.e.*, in today's world, the supermarket. And ordinarily we
mix other foods with our vegetables, which tends to reduce
the potency of any poisonous plant we might eat. Most
people have nurtured the plants for their beauty without
knowing of their poisons, and even today seed and nursery
catalogues do not often reveal the dangerous possibilities
in some of the items offered for sale. In earlier times many
herbs were known to have, or assumed to have, medicinal
properties, but only a very few were known to be poisonous. In fact, it is only in the last 150 years that the toxic
nature of most dangerous plants has become known. Yet,
according to one authority, each year thousands of people
in North America require medical treatment because of
such plants, and the death toll to grazing animals is in the
hundreds of thousands.[1]

The adult, because of his reliance on his greengrocer,
is not prone, unless of a very curious bent, to eat wild or
ornamental plants. But young children are naturally inquisitive and are always eating rather odd things. And, as
has been pointed out, babies by instinct will put almost
anything into their mouths. This is where the greatest
danger in ignorance about poisonous plants lies. Who
knows how many babies and children, who have died in
convulsions, had been poisoned by some leaves or berries
they had eaten?

[1] John M. Kingsbury, *Deadly Harvest. A Guide to Common
Poisonous Plants* (New York, Holt, Rinehart and Winston, 1965),
p. 7.

In 1955, when the baby Terence Armstrong died in England and tiny red shells were found in his stomach at the autopsy, it was first suspected that he might have consumed berries from the daphne tree which overhung his carriage. After further examination, however, these shells turned out to be capsules of the Seconal with which the infant had been murdered—the first recorded use of a barbiturate for homicide.[2] It required the illness of children to reveal, only recently, the toxic properties of wisteria, after which cases which had been previously unreported—out of some inexplicable scientific diffidence— came to light and corroborated the findings. Today the sweet pea, beloved of maiden ladies and some others, is under grave suspicion and investigation.

Young children must be instructed not to eat any leaves, seeds, nuts, berries or roots they find in the garden, the streets or the woods, but only the vegetables and other food served by their parents. In the same way that they should be warned against sampling the contents of bottles and containers in the bathroom medicine chest or the kitchen closet, they should be warned against the vegetable kingdom. At a slightly later age, if they should become boy scouts or girl scouts, they will get instructions on the poisonous plants to be avoided on their hikes and camping trips. But when even adults, because of their ignorance, poison themselves accidentally with plants, the need for broader knowledge about them continues.

Little enough is known about plants as food and it has only been since the last century that more than a handful of poisonous plants were identified as such. In fact, some of our common table vegetables contain poisons —cabbage, turnips, lima beans, spinach, beet greens, onions, rhubarb leaves, tomatoes and potatoes (especially

[2] Jürgen Thorwald, *The Century of the Detective*, trans. by Richard and Clara Winston, A Helen and Kurt Wolff Book (New York, Harcourt, Brace and World, Inc., 1965), p. 382 ff.

the green "sunburned" spots and the sprouts), but the level of toxicity is not harmful unless the vegetables are consumed in great quantities. In January of this year a scientist announced that he had isolated a poison named carotatoxin from celery and carrots, and that the pure alkaloid had killed daphnia, minute water creatures, in seconds. But there is a consolation for human beings: a man would have to eat ten times his own weight at a sitting before the vegetables would harm him. There is on record however an instance of a man who so loved apple seeds that he saved them from each apple he ate in order to have a true banquet on a whole cupful. Soon after his taste treat he died, for the seeds contain cyanide.

At present, with scientific researches still incomplete, more than 700 dangerous plants are known to grow in this hemisphere. But, you may say, most of these are weeds and wild grasses and would not be planted in our gardens. Still, weeds do appear in gardens and people do go into the woods for recreation among all sorts of unknown vegetation. We tend to imagine that most plants are harmless, simply unpalatable greenery which we would not use as vegetables. Thoreau ate a great deal of this unfamiliar vegetation when he was living beside Walden Pond and did not suffer from it. Most of us know enough to avoid the poison ivy varieties, and we know that useful drugs are extracted from plants. We do not, probably, admit that the drugs are medically tested and controlled dosages of what are actually poisons in their pure state. We deceive ourselves with love and sympathy for nature. We imagine that plants have developed poisons as a protection against destruction by herbivores, as we imagine that the poison of a jellyfish is a compensation for its having no bones or fins to protect it. Or we think the poisonous plant should be ugly and the harmless one beautiful. Unfortunately, the strange chemistry of plants does not operate in that way. And adults, ironically, have been forced to a wider and more thorough knowledge of the toxic substances in plants by the mistakes of animals and children: stricken animals have drawn attention to the wild vegetation; sick or dying children to the ornamentals in our gardens.

Our knowledge of the toxic properties in plants was much expanded during the eighteenth and nineteenth centuries. Before that time the recognized poisons were mostly metallic and mineral—arsenic, antimony, mercury and phosphorous—with a few herbal poisons. The Mesopotamians knew of henbane, castor oil and mandrake. To these the Greeks added hemlock, aconite and hellebore. By contrast, on the other side of the world the Asian Indians by the second century could list 500 medicinal plants (not all poisonous, of course) and in Susruta's book there are 760. But in the Western world the knowledge of toxicology was limited until the twelfth century; by then the doctors (and witches, too) knew also of the fatal powers of opium, spurge, thorn apple, hemp, nightshade and belladonna. But no one knew what the toxic principle was in these plants. For homicide the favorite poison remained arsenic, because it is odorless and tasteless and produces symptoms very like those of cholera. There was no method of determining from a corpse whether it held a large dose of poison, and obviously thousands of deaths attributed to natural causes and diseases could, in truth, have been caused by poisons. In the days of the Borgias, the Marquise de Brinvilliers and Madonna Teofania di Adamo, arsenic was known as "inheritance powder"; if one wanted to inherit money or a title, one speeded the process by using arsenic. It is certainly possible that the common people used it to gain their ends as well.

With the rapid advances in the application of chemical knowledge, scientists were able by 1850 to deal with most of the mineral and metallic poisons but the plant poisons were more elusive because the toxic principles were not known. But in 1805 morphine was isolated from opium, in 1819 strychnine from *nux vomica*, in 1826 conine from hemlock, in 1828 nicotine from tobacco, in 1833 atropine from deadly nightshade, to be followed in later years by almost two thousand more plant poisons. Most of these are called alkaloids and their names are usually derived from the botanical names of the plants. Others are termed glycosides, indicating the presence of sugar in compound with other substances. While doctors learned to use the new plant poisons for therapeutic purposes, they also became the first to use them for murder. Plant poisons vanish in the body tissues and the use of the poison for homicide could not be proven a century ago. Faced with this knowledge, the prosecutor in the first trial for murder by morphine (the accused was Dr. Edmé Castaing) said bitterly: "Since plant poisons leave no traces behind, murder by such poisons is not punishable. . . . Use plant poisons. Murderers, poison your fathers, poison your mothers; poison your whole families, and enjoy your inheritance. Fear nothing; your crime will go unpunished."[3] There seems no reason to doubt that his advice was taken seriously by countless people whose murders of others were neither suspected nor detected.

The progress of toxicology did not halt with satisfying, though still incomplete, knowledge of the natural poisons found upon the earth. Chemists went on to invent synthetic poisons in barbiturates, insecticides and insulin, and one is at a loss to guess what may come next.

II

By close definition a poison is a substance having an inherent harmful property which, when placed in the mouth, swallowed or in any way absorbed into the blood, is able to impair health or destroy life. It may be in the

[3] Thorwald, *op. cit.*, pp. 274, 292–295.

form of a liquid, a solid or a gas. It may originate in animal, vegetable or mineral, and if that makes one think of a guessing game, the relevant question is too often not "Which?" but "Will he live?" There is also bacterial poison, such as botulin, which unlike the others has no commercial use and as yet, apparently, little homicidal or suicidal currency.

The animal poisons, usually called venom, come from bites or stings of insects, reptiles or sea life such as wasps, bees, hornets, spiders, tarantulas, scorpions, centipedes, Gila monsters, worms, caterpillars, snakes, vipers, eels, morays, sea urchins, sting rays and jellyfish. Animal poisons have also been derived by man from creatures such as snakes, toads, salamanders and porcupine-fish for various destructive ends. But whereas poisons derived from plants or minerals have for centuries been adapted to various medicinal and commercial uses, it is only recently that the venom of rattlesnakes has been extracted for therapeutic purposes.

Some vegetable and mineral poisons are rather similar as to chemical composition and sometimes produce similar symptoms. The mineral poisons, those derived by chemical processes from minerals as acids, salts, compounds or solutions, are generally caustic or corrosive, whereas the plant poisons usually are not. Most of the latter attack the functioning of the nervous system or the organs—the heart, lungs, kidneys or liver. The overlapping of classifications by effects, physical characteristics or chemical analyses, contributes to a tangled ball of threads whose complexities I can only try to suggest, rather than neatly unravel.

Consider, for instance, a dozen of the most dangerous poisons of a caustic or corrosive nature: hydrochloric acid, sulphuric acid, nitric acid, carbolic acid, oxalic acid, salt of oxalic acid, acetic acid, hypochlorous acid, sodium hydroxide, potassium hydroxide, ammonium hydroxide

and silver nitrate. These, except for three, are all derived
from minerals through chemical processes. Acetic acid
is the essential constituent of vinegar, which comes ulti-
mately from such fruits as grapes and apples, and you will
see on the label of your bottle of table vinegar a statement
of the percentage of acidity (usually 5 percent). Oxalic
acid and its salts were first found in the juice of the wood
sorrel (*Oxalis acetosella*), though the acid is manufactured chemically today. And oddly enough, ammonium
hydroxide, a compound of ammonia and water, reaches
back to origins in an animal, the male deer; hartshorn, the
antler of the hart, figured prominently. in the ancient
pharmacopoeia as a source of ammonia.

The corrosive poisons destroy any tissues which they
touch, but when diluted they become what is called, with
stoic good humor, "irritant" poisons. That is, instead of
eating furiously at tissues, they merely cause an inflammation and often a lingering, though just as often a swift,
death. Among the genuine undiluted irritant poisons are
the arsenic so dear to murderers, and its relative, antimony. And, to range far afield, there is the lead tetraethyl
which girds the gasoline in your automobile to kill the
knocks in its engine. But don't inhale its fumes—too much
will give an unpleasant knock to your own health.

Among the poisons which affect one or another of the
systems or organs of the body—the systemic poisons as
they are called—is one of the deadliest and, for that
obvious reason, I suppose, one of the best known. It kills
almost instantly—not only man and animals, but all forms
of living matter. The name might well be remembered,
since it will come up in later pages as one of the toxic
principles in plants: cyanide. In compounds it appears
under the names of hydrocyanic acid, prussic acid and, in
memory of the Swedish chemist who discovered it in 1782,
Scheele's acid. It has a distinctive odor of bitter almond,
which will not be noticeable in the plants secreting it,

since the poison is much diluted in them and mixed with other substances. However, in the form of glycosides, the poison is found in small or large proportions in many plants. When a person has swallowed a fatal amount of this poison, the *Encyclopaedia Britannica* tells us that, before his face turns blue, "occasionally the victim may be able to perform a few voluntary actions before loss of consciousness," in case that is a consolation. All this, however, refers to the relatively pure state of the acid and it will not be found in such violent toxicity, fortunately, in the plants which contain it.

A second important poison found in plants is strychnine, a common ingredient of rat and roach exterminators. The poison goes to work reasonably fast—within ten or fifteen minutes—and is announced by a stiffness in the neck and a terrified countenance. The head then jerks back, the arms and legs stretch out and the back rears in an arch with the body resting on heels and head. This is followed by relaxation of the muscles and later returns of the spasm.

Probably the most potent of poisons, though not so well known as the cyanides, is aconitine, of which as little as four milligrams has caused a man's death. This frightening alkaloid, which must at some time have delighted or tempted Alfred Hitchcock's TV heart, is found in the aconite, commonly known as monkshood or wolfsbane, a pretty flowering plant of the poisonous Delphinium family. Delphinium and larkspur, however, secrete a different toxic alkaloid. Aconitine causes burning, tingling and numbness in the body, depression and finally stoppage of the heart.

Belladonna is familiar to anyone who has had his eyes dilated for examination by a doctor. For a poison and its source (*Atropa belladonna*) to be described as "fair lady" is ironic, but it happened so because the ladies of the Renaissance used the drops in their eyes to enlarge the pupils for beauty's sake. The common name of the plant, deadly nightshade, more accurately reflects its characteristics. To this family of plants also belong henbane, mandrake, jimsonweed, tobacco and—good heavens!—potatoes, tomatoes and petunias. The latter three are not dangerously toxic, though it has been pointed out that potatoes and tomatoes do contain small amounts of cyanide.

As to the tomato, let me digress to sketch the curious story of my favorite berry—for that is what the tomato is. A native of the American tropics, it was discovered by the Spanish invaders under cultivation in the gardens of the Mayas, Aztecs and Incas, who called it *tomatl.* The Spaniards took seeds back to their homeland and the plant was grown in Morocco. When the Italians imported the tomato they called it *pomo dei mori,* "apple of the Moors," and when the French got it from the Italians they—typically, one might say—corrupted the Italian name into *pomme d'amour,* "apple of love," and dubbed it an aphrodisiac. At length the plant reached England with its name at least correctly translated from the French, and as the "love-apple"—a name it still bears—it returned to this continent with the colonists. Through most of this time, however, because of its membership in the nightshade family, it was considered poisonous and grown only as an ornamental plant. John Gerard, in his *Herball* of 1597, describes the red and the yellow fruited kinds he grew and sums up the virtues of the fruit: "In Spaine and those hot Regions they use to eate the Apples prepared and boiled with pepper, salt, and oyle: but they yield very little nourishment to the body, and the same naught and corrupt. Likewise they doe eate the Apples with oile, vinegre and pepper mixed together for sauce to their meat, even as we in these cold countries doe Mustard." At least *somebody* outside the Mayan races had discovered the delicious tomato! But it was not till around 1830 that the superstition and fear which had surrounded the "love-apple" were dissipated and it became a staple article of food in England and the United States.

Opium which, usually in derivatives, has widespread medicinal uses, is the dried juice of the seed capsules of the poppy (*Papaver somniferum*). It is familiar to most people through reading Thomas De Quincey, or through fiction, plays, movies and, until recently, tourist trips through San Francisco's Chinatown where, in a stage-set room, Orientals were exhibited practicing their vice in an "opium den." I don't doubt that real such "dens" existed nearby, for opium is a powerful addictive drug which induces, we are told, a sense of euphoria and delightful dreams. However, too large a dose induces death. Its principle narcotic element is morphine; tincture of opium is called laudanum. From morphine is derived the even more toxic heroin, which our contemporary young rebels and reformers, from beatniks to undergraduates, call "snow" and other less chaste names.

Also familiar to the new generation as "snow" is another powerful drug of addiction, cocaine. It is the active alkaloid of the leaves of the coca plant, a shrub native to the Andes of Peru. Though it has been introduced into Java for commercial purposes, its spread has been limited. It is unlikely that you will have the shrub in your garden or find it on sale at a greenhouse nursery. Small quantities of cocaine were used in confections and beverages in the past but the practice has been discontinued, both voluntarily and by law. Incidentally, cola, the word frequently combined with a prefix of some sort, did not originally mean a soft drink but is the name of an African plant which contains caffeine.

The last of the more important plant poisons, and of the stimulant-depressant drugs which can cause death (though rarely so in this case) is—heaven protect me from the tobacco industry!—nicotine. This is an alkaloid from the plant *Nicotiana tabacum*, but it is also prevalent in other species of the genus *Nicotiana*, which are wild or cultivated in flower gardens. The commercial products of tobacco allow for absorption of nicotine by inhalation of cigar, pipe, cigarette or snuff fumes and by ingestion of the juices of chewing tobacco. Taking moderate amounts of nicotine in some form is obviously agreeable, for millions of people do so, but an immoderate amount taken into the system will cause oppression and irregularity of the heartbeat, nausea and other unpleasant symptoms. Harmful though it is, it nevertheless provides us with a derivative, nicotinic acid (or niacin), which is a component of the vitamin B complex and of the popular one-a-day vitamins.

Poisonous gases need not concern us long. A few are produced naturally: the gas found under the earth in petroleum regions, marsh gas, chokedamp or afterdamp in coal mines, the carbonic acid gases which frequently form in cellars, wells, etc., and sewer gas. Others are more direct products or by-products of man's activities: coal gas, water gas, fumes from gas heaters, smoky stoves and automobiles—carbon monoxides all. A third group includes man's deliberate inventions by means of chemical processes. They are for use in warfare and range from tear gas to lethal gases such as phosgene and mustard gas. Mustard gas, despite its name, is not derived from the mustard plant but bears a close resemblance to mustard oil. As to plants and gas, however, those who are old enough to recall the days of World War I may remember how peach stones were saved up for use in that first era of warfare by poisonous gases.

Vapors such as chloroform and ether have the dual nature of being either helpful or harmful depending on their use. Curiously, arsenic can in some way pass through the air and contaminate a person if the circumstances are right. Not many years ago we were surprised to learn that our ambassadress to the Vatican, Claire Booth Luce, had complained of being poisoned by the ceiling paint in her apartments. Perhaps this charge seemed absurd and amused many people. But it is known that a room covered with paper on which arsenical dyes have been used can produce the symptoms of poisoning. Beyond this area we move into a realm of suppositions and legends, the most recent one being that the deadly oleander emits dangerous odors if kept in a closed room.

The blossom whose very odor—or gas—is deadly is a legendary notion, very likely an extension of the knowledge of the actual poisonous properties of certain plants. I have heard of a tree in Florida under which it is dangerous to take refuge during a rainstorm; this may be the manchineel, a tree that figures prominently in Meyerbeer's opera, *L'Africaine*. According to the *Victrola Book of the Opera* (7th ed., 1924), in Act IV a group of women is marched off "to the deadly grove of mancinilla trees, whose influence is poison"; and in the final scene of Act V the heroine "seizes some of the deadly flowers, and inhales the perfume," after which her rejected lover arrives and "drinks of the poisoned air of the flowers and sinks beside her." Alexander Pushkin's poem, "The Upas Tree," describes the *Antiaris toxicaria* of the Orient, shunned in fear of death by birds and tigers. In Francesco Cilea's opera, *Adriana Lecouvreur*, the heroine smells a bunch of poisoned violets and, after spasms, delirium and a final aria, dies. The actual Adrienne (1692–1730) was sent poisoned lozenges but warily tried them out on an unfortunate dog. Obviously a change was needed for opera— how can a soprano sing while chewing a lozenge? So it happens that in Delibes' opera, Lakmé seems on the stage to be inhaling a flower; but the libretto clearly says that she eats the flowers of *Datura*. Jimsonweed, for heaven's sake! The concept of the deadly odor of flowers was not only given much credence in earlier times, but it was plainly very serviceable to theatre craftsmen in providing poetic imagery and action on the stage.

## III

Though it is true that on reading, or merely leafing through, a compendium of plants—weeds, grasses and cultivated flowers—which are noxious or fatal to man and animal, one may be filled with amazement that the human race and the grazing beasts have survived, it should be remembered that many things have served to keep the fatalities at a fairly low level. Still, no more will I walk through dense woods bewaring only of poison ivies and nettles. No more will I believe so easily that it is ingenuity and not sheer Providence which saves the lives of those we read of from time to time, who have been lost for days in the wilds and managed to survive on, as they tell us, berries, fruits and nuts. I, at least, having studied the subject of poison plants, would never come through except in a state of starvation.

As to the factors which protect us to some degree, probably the greatest is that of the 300,000 plants known only a few, especially of those used as ornamentals, are deadly. And poisonous plants, like people, have many peculiarities. Some are toxic only in certain parts—berries, seeds, leaves or roots—and some lose their poisons when cooked. Some are more poisonous at one season of the year or one stage of growth than at others. Their toxicity may vary in accordance with the section of the country they grow in (east or west), with the geological differences in soil, with the amount of rainfall, with the gender of the plant, and even with the condition of the leaves—whether they are crisp and fresh or cut and wilted. On the other hand it has been discovered that some nonpoisonous plants have been contaminated by neighboring poisonous ones through a chemical chain. The poisonous plant absorbs selenium from the soil (as the innocent plants can not do) and in dying and decomposing, leaves the selenium in a changed state—predigested, so to speak—so that the harmless plants can, during the next season, draw the toxic substance into their own systems.

One of the more unusual effects of some poisons is a "sunburn" or, accurately, photosensitization. Mankind is not entirely immune, but most cases occur among animals—cattle and sheep—and only among animals with white skin and hair. Black and white coated animals burn only in the white areas. In certain plants (buckwheat, St. Johnswort, puncture vine, lantana, for example) there are chemical compounds which once inside the body introduce an "abnormal pigment" into the blood, thereby affecting the blood vessels and making the skin sensitive to light. The diseased parts swell with fluids and in severe cases the animals can lose their ears and lips and lives. Sheep ranchers call the affliction "bighead." A similar relation between poison and hair color was reported by John W. Harshberger in reference to redroot (*Lachnanthes tinctoria*) which he claimed strikes down only white pigs and tints their bones reddish pink, "so that there develops a preponderance of black pigs over white ones in regions where the plant is abundant." Later research and experiments failed to corroborate his statements.

Some people are more susceptible to certain poisons than others are. Children, not surprisingly when one thinks how dosages of medicine are reduced for them, and the aged and the ill are most vulnerable. Only last year, it has been reported, at least 150 children were killed by aspirin. Some people have particular allergies—those most familiar to us are abnormal sensitivity to ragweed, goldenrod, roses and even cats—but one of the less known is a hyper-susceptibility to bee stings. Most people are only momentarily and slightly injured by them and it has been estimated that about five hundred stings would be required to kill the average man. A case has been recorded of a doctor's wife who almost died of a wasp sting, but the poison was injected directly into her carotid artery, making its effect more immediate and powerful. Yet some people have died from an ordinary bee sting, simply because they were allergic to it. This extraordinary fact was used as the basis for a murder story called "Where Is Thy Sting?" by James Holding. On the other hand, some people can develop a tolerance for poisons—arsenic, morphine, opium, cocaine and alcohol, for example.

But must we take the joy out of life by thinking of tobacco and alcohol as poisons? We do have a tolerance for small amounts of them. I know of no cases of death caused primarily by the nicotine in tobacco smoke although the development of lung cancer is widely held to be a result of its continued absorption, but death from pure nicotinic acid is easily brought about as will be seen later. Death from alcohol, even in diluted form as we drink it, is not unusual. Periodically we read of some broth of a boy who wagers he can drink a quart of whisky all at once. And for the money he does—and dies. Cases involving the addictive drugs including the synthetic barbiturates need not be stressed; they are so numerous and so frequent as to be alarming and, unhappily, not surprising. As to arsenic, the best example is probably the one dramatized in a one-act play popular some years ago, *A Game of Chess,* by Kenneth Sawyer Goodman, in which a man who has inured himself to arsenic succeeds in killing his enemy with it, though both drink the same wine. The huge Russian monk, Rasputin, seemed to have a tolerance not only for lethal prussic acid (cakes and wine poisoned with it simply made him ill), but for bullets. When the poison failed to kill him at once, he was shot but still stubbornly remained alive; he was finally thrown into the river to drown. These are matters of susceptibility or, in the case of plants causing dermatitis, allergy.

Still another factor which protects us and the herbivores from continual poisoning is that most of the plants are not appetizing. Man has learned much from his long centuries of experience and knows, in normal circumstances, what vegetation to eat. To a degree, the grazing herds know this too and will not eat any bitter, toxic herbage unless there is scant vegetation on the pasture lands or unless the poisonous plants grow mixed in with harmless grasses. As a matter of fact, most of the poisonous plants of the United States are apparently wild weeds, grasses and shrubs whose toxic properties have become known because of the accidental poisoning of stock on the ranges. In this exploration the veterinarians, supported by the botanists and biochemists, have probably contributed most. It was through investigation of livestock poisoning by molded sweet clover, which caused unnatural bleeding internally and under the skin, that a substance called coumarin was discovered. From this was developed the anticoagulant medicine, dicoumarin, which was used in combating President Eisenhower's heart attack in 1958.[4]

Many garden plants, however, have been nurtured for centuries and something of their virtues, lethal or healing, has been known from ancient times, especially to early scientists, alchemists, sorcerers, witches, medicine men, and herb doctors. Today we have more accurate and more extensive knowledge about all plants' virtues, whether they are poisonous or medicinal, nourishing or merely delicious to eat, fragrant to smell, lovely to look at.

For poisons, and poisonous plants, like people, have their double natures: they can be noxious or healing, just as people can be obnoxious or lovable. We can no more exterminate them to any advantage than we can exterminate people. Even the most "poisonous" person contributes something to man's knowledge of himself by showing how

[4] Kingsbury, *op. cit.*, pp. 90–91.

evil man *can* be and by creating revulsion for such evil actions.

While poisons may kill if used ignorantly, at the same time they furnish the medicines—the judicious use of poisons, so to speak—which cure our diseases. "Venom destroys venom," wrote William Langland in the fourteenth century; and Ben Jonson, three centuries later, amplified those words with "while two poisons wrestle we may live." Though unscientific by the standards of our advanced twentieth century knowledge, they were, nevertheless, correct in their general theory. For some poisons are used not only to combat others but controlled dosages are used to combat bacterial and viral poisons, which we call diseases. We should understand this and should understand the properties of plants for good—or for ill if used in ignorance. Let us keep the beautiful plants which are favorites in our dooryards, backyards, terraces or indoor gardens, but let us be aware of the potential danger hidden in them and using this knowledge avoid the possibility of accidents.

## IV

The overall plan of this book has been to treat those poisonous plants which might fall within the boundaries of the average home garden. However, since many highly poisonous plants are weeds and would appear only by accident in the ordinary garden, a section has been given to some of these more notorious, as well as glamorous and historic, intruders. Finally, given our progressively more urban culture, the whole concept of "garden" had to be reconsidered. Millions of people in recent years have been uprooted—like plants—and transferred from communities where they lived in private houses with surrounding or adjacent gardens to cramped cities where they live in duplexes or apartments and, if they are wealthy enough, may have cindery backyards, terraces, tiny balconies or merely picture windowsills on which to continue their relationship with the world of growing and blossoming plants. Thus, a section touching on some of the plants particularly adapted to growing inside the homes of city-dwellers had to be added. A final section deals with plants which are subject to serious suspicion but about which not enough is yet known to warrant a separate discussion of each one.

The book is not intended to be a comprehensive technical study of poisonous plants, or even of the plants to which it is limited. It is a survey of information and, perhaps, a warning signal. Though it is not directed toward botanists, to whom it can contribute nothing new, I hope it will not offend them in the loose terminology I use—for example, not distinguishing between sepals and petals—and that they will understand that the gardening enthusiast usually speaks in general terms. Aside from such popular usage, I am confident that errors—all small ones, I trust—are scattered through this work, and I hope I can be confident that experts will, in a spirit of tolerance for the amateur, point them out, in the expectation that they can be corrected in any subsequent edition of the book.

Within its restricted space this book cannot offer accurate botanical specifications or the symptoms of poisoning by the various plants or the best remedies. To the average reader, I fear the scientific descriptions would be largely meaningless, certainly colorless, and the symptoms of poisoning would become redundant and unpleasant. These details are given in the definitive and authoritative works of the late Walter C. Muenscher and of John M. Kingsbury, which I recommend to any whose interest has been whetted by my summary of the subject.

As to remedies, antidotes and first aid in case of poisoning, I would not dare to attempt setting these down, for fear that someone might rely on them. There are some ground rules, though, which can be put here, as to what to do in case of suspected poisoning. First, call your doctor—urgent! Even minutes can sometimes save a life. Keep the patient in bed, warm, quiet if possible. In most instances of plant poisoning, it seems advisable to induce vomiting. A tablespoonful of salt in a glass of warm water is a safe emetic—if indeed one *is* safe in the circumstances—but is to be used *only* if the patient is conscious. Most poisonous plants cause vomiting in any case and often diarrhea. If you don't know what plant is involved, it is important that you save the vomit and stools for the doctor to examine.

From this you can see that, as Dr. Kingsbury points out more eloquently than I do, your duty, especially if you have children, is to know the poisonous plants around your neighborhood, and their names, even in botanical Latin. In this connection, I want to support the plea in his recent book, *Deadly Harvest*, that such lethal seeds as castor beans in packets and precatory beans made into necklaces and bracelets should be labelled, when put on sale, as poisonous. If cigarettes must carry such a warning, why not more immediately deadly substances? The same warning might well be used, with explanations, on packets of flower seeds whenever the potential danger in the resulting plant is high.

I am neither botanist, chemist, toxicologist nor physician—only an amateur gardener—and have written this book in the hope of arousing more serious interest in poisonous plants and drawing more attention to the problems they create around us than they have received in the past. As I hope any reader of the following pages will realize, even when I score up a heavy case of death against some plant or other, nevertheless I do love plants and flowers. And I trust that what I say will not move the reader to flee from plants in terror, but will stimulate him to a deeper interest in their fascinating displays, histories and powers.

# Acknowledgments

I am deeply indebted to the studies of the late Dr. Walter C. Muenscher and of Dr. John M. Kingsbury on poisonous plants, as well as to the books of the other authors listed in the bibliography. In addition I wish to acknowledge the generous help of the many friends who have contributed references, data, hints, suggestions, reminiscences and books for my work on this volume. From among them I must list for especial thanks James A. Beard, Jeannette Bruce, Douglas Cooke, Lillian de la Torre, Sonya Dorman, John Ferrone, Maurice Grosser, Barbara Howes, Robert S. MacKellar, Mr. and Mrs. Bill F. Middlebrooks, Joseph P. Morris, Dorothy Crayder Newman, Robert Newman, Princess Mary de Rachwiltz, Stephen Rome, Mr. and Mrs. John V. Schaffner, William Jay Smith, Frank Waggoner, Ben Weber, Eudora Welty, Mr. and Mrs. Robert Wilbur, James N. Wise, Constance Wright; thanks also to Mary Clemmey for special research, and to my editor, Edward Burlingame, who thought of the book in the first place.

# The Garden

# *Amaryllis—The Daffodil Family*

## *Amaryllidaceae*

*N*arcissus and daffodil are the more popular and better
known plants of the poisonous *Amaryllis* family,
but some of the less prominent members of this small but
toxic family should be noted as well. *Amaryllis* was once
a genus of the natural order *Liliaceae*, but because of
certain structural differences it is now classified as a
separate family from the lilies.

The major distinction between the two families is
that the lily has a "superior ovary" (a reference to place-
ment, not quality) and the amaryllis an "inferior" one. A
superior ovary is "free from all surrounding parts of the
flower"; if you look into the trumpet of a lily you will
probably see it easily, a swollen bead at the base of the
style where the petals join the stem. An inferior ovary is
"surrounded by and inseparably joined with the basal
parts of the flower or the expanded tip of the flower stalk."
This can be felt just below the sepals of a blossoming
amaryllis, narcissus or snowdrop.

The handsome, almost flagrantly showy blossoms
of the large amaryllis bulb (*A. belladonna* and other
varieties) appear in pots in florist shops each early spring
and are a familiar sight. In the South they can be planted

in outdoor beds, but in the North they are unable to survive the winters. The great flaring trumpets of amaryllises
appear in threes and fours at the top of a single naked
stalk, usually before the broad strap-like leaves have pro-
gressed very far. A lucky owner may be granted two
flowering stalks from one bulb. The blossoms come in a
variety of colors; some with stripes down the center of
each petal.

The plant originated in the tropics of this hemisphere
but most of those sold today are hybrids. With few excep-
tions, the more spectacular amaryllises were imported into
the United States and other Western countries from tropical Africa and Asia. Some, of course, have come from
the West Indies, Mexico and South America and a few
can claim species native to the United States. But most
of those favorites of flower lovers must be treated, in their
new homes, as house or greenhouse plants.

The plant called "hardy amaryllis," *Lycoris*, is a
relative which comes to us from China and Japan and
can be grown as far north as New England. Depending
upon the species, it is yellow, red, rose-pink or white,
fragrant or not; and the red or white type (*L. radiata*) is
the source of lycorine (first isolated in 1899), which is a
too common alkaloid in the family *Amaryllidaceae*.

Two other relatives which are reasonably hardy, if
given dry cellar storage in regions with severe winters, are
the spider lily (*Hymenocallis americana*), and the "Peruvian daffodil" (*H. calathina*), sometimes called the basket
flower. The latter species is from the Andes of Peru and
Bolivia, as its name indicates, but the first is a native of
our American South. As a man who has long been bored
with the American merchandising passion for doubling
everything, from double-rich foods to double-petalled
flowers, all the while vitiating the essential qualities, I
prefer our native specimen. This is not to say that the
Peruvian *Hymenocallis* is double-flowered; but it is lush

compared to the spider lily though it is beautiful in its own way. Its umbel of large white funnel-shaped cups with six green stripes terminating in inward-curving stamens at the lip and recurving spathes around the corolla is pleasing. The North American spider lily is, to me, more elegant and more fascinating, but not so pure white. The whole structure of the blossom curves upward from the stem, the six long spathes seemingly trying to grasp over the center of the flower and the six stamens reaching out and up from the ragged edges of a shallow saucer of white web, forming its ribs. It is very simple and very unreal. I am not alone in favoring this plant, for it is often found in Southern gardens as well as in its wild habitat, but I think I have a particular fascination with it because of both its common and its botanical names. It projects the abstract image, florally, of a spider; *Hymenocallis* is a Greek compound meaning the "beautiful membrane," which one sees in the flattened saucer; and one is also reminded of the Greek god of marriage, Hymen. What a combination of flower references—beauty, marriage, spiders—and to have to add to those, poison!

Two smaller hardy members of the daffodil tribe which are more modest but lovable to me, are the snowdrop (*Galanthus nivalis*) and snowflake (*Leucojum aestivum*), both introduced from Europe and Asia Minor, and both popular early spring blossoming plants for the border or for naturalizing. There are only a few technical differences to set them apart from other amaryllises, but for the scientist they exist. The flowers, white with green markings at the tips of the petals, droop from the top of a short stem and, when looked at from certain angles, suggest white bees about to take flight. The bulbs of snowdrop as well as hyacinth and narcissus poisoned livestock in the Netherlands during World War II.

The eastern United States has a pretty member of the daffodil family which is a hardy native, resembling a lily.

In fact, it is called Easter lily (wild), Atamasco lily (*Zephyranthes Atamasco*), or zephyr lily. From a small bulb it puts up thin grassy leaves and a clean stalk with one or two simple, charming little funnel-shaped white flowers. The species I have always particularly liked in a garden has a pink or rose flower (*Z. grandiflora*) and I called it "rain lily" because it always bloomed—and swiftly—after a rain, or sometimes if the deception were good enough, after a wetting with the hose. Horses are thought to have suffered the disease called "staggers" after eating this little plant. At present, however, not a great deal is known about its toxic nature.

The oddest member of the daffodil family is our native century plant (*Agave americana*), whose legend holds, erroneously as I know at my age, that it blooms only once in a hundred years. The fact is that most agaves bloom infrequently; the century plant blooms—stupendously—after ten years or so and then dies. Agaves, which need a rather tropical dry climate, grow wild in the Southwest and produce a rosette of gray, thorn-tipped, dagger-shaped, spiny-edged leaves—each as long as six feet. When they do bloom, a stalk, scaly like a giant asparagus, rises to perhaps forty feet and puts forth a series of branches at the top, holding pads of yellowish flowers—really rather like scrubbing brushes. Other forms of agave are, by comparison, tiny, and may appear in "dish gardens."

Along with yucca, another huge rosette of dagger leaves, the agaves are being relegated to a family of their own, the *Agavaceae*. But yuccas are usually classed in the lily family and agaves in the daffodil family. Technical reasons have been given for this move to transfer, but I think—privately—that they were just too prickly a matter to be left with lilies and daffodils.

Both these giant thorny plants are presently undergoing investigation by research scientists on plant drugs.

Saponin compounds (soapy glycosides of steroid structure which destroy red blood cells) have been found abundantly in both but the practical application of them has not been learned. One species of agave (*A. lecheguilla*), which grows in the Southwest and Mexico, is a menace to grazing animals, since, because it contains saponins, it is a photodynamic plant and causes "bighead" in sheep. In general, however, the agaves have been a boon to the ancient people of Mexico, providing them with, among other items, paper, fiber, thread and stimulants (pulque, tequila and mescal). I don't think for a moment that any adult or child would brave those thorns and spines to chew upon such large, fibrous, though juicy, leaves, and thereby become photosensitized.

It is a different matter, however, with the bulbous members of *Amaryllidaceae*. Most of those previously mentioned—the spider lilies, snowdrops and snowflakes as well as the narcissus and daffodil types—have smallish bulbs which, if left on a table or shelf, could easily be eaten by a child or, as has happened, be mistaken for onions. This is not quite the case with the popular spectacularly flowered "lilies" in this family. Most of them have large, dark, scaly bulbs and might not be attractive to a child. Since they are imported from tropical regions of South America, Africa and Asia, they can only be planted outdoors in the far South or on the southern Pacific coast.

Unfortunately, however, many of them are known to contain poisons. Among these dangerous bulbs are the handsome *Crinum* lilies (there is an American species, *C. americanum*, in the southern swamplands); the South African *Nerine* lilies (one of the best known is called Guernsey lily); and the blood lilies (*Haemanthus*). Most people will have them in pots, but they should not be unaware of the toxic nature of the bulbs inside.

# *Autumn Crocus*

## *Colchicum autumnale*

*T*he familiar names we apply to plants, based on sim-
ilarities of leaf, flower or aromatic oils, usually lead to
confusion. Autumn crocus is not a true crocus at all but
a lily. One of its common names is meadow saffron; but
saffron, which was introduced into Spain in the Middle
Ages by the Moors, is a true crocus (*Crocus sativus*) and
a member of the iris family. Its name was derived from
the Arabian word *zafaran*. Meadow saffron and saffron
crocus have similar leaves and flowers but while both
grow from corms, bulb-like bases of the stem, the lanceo-
late leaves of meadow saffron are noticeably broader, and
they mature and wither before the flower appears in
autumn—alone on its stalk; the true crocus usually blooms
in spring along with its grassy leaves. To compound the
confusion there is also an autumn-flowering true crocus.
Perhaps the important distinction is, aside from the uses
of the plants, that the true crocus has three stamens which
push outward between the petals, and the meadow saffron
has six. There is also a plant named safflower, of a third
different family, the composites, which has such common
names as fake, bastard or wild saffron, and saffron-thistle.
But of that, more later.

*Colchicum autumnale*

The poisonous meadow saffron or autumn crocus should be called by its botanical name, Colchicum, in commemoration of its early legends. The plant is supposed to have first sprung from liquor which that arch-witch Medea spilled on the ground when she was restoring Aeson to youth. Medea, daughter of King Aeëtes, lived in Colchis, a land on the eastern shores of the Black Sea, and there and in her travels left a flotsam of dead people in her wake—all destroyed by her magic and her knowledge of herbs. One must or at least wishes to—assume that Colchicum, the autumn crocus, was one of her potent drug plants.

The blossoms of this amazing bulb are whitish or shade into pale lilac and mauve, and their habit of appearing after the foliage has disappeared has earned them the common name of "naked ladies"—unless the name subtly alludes to some inherent danger. This curious life cycle teased Gerard's mind, and he wrote that the meadow saffron "bringeth forth leaves in Februarie, seed in May, and floures in September; which is a thing cleane contrarie to all other plants whatsoever." Gilbert White, too, was awed by it; in *The Natural History of Selborne* (letter written in 1778) he said of the plant's nature: "This circumstance is one of the wonders of the creation, little noticed, because a common occurrence: yet ought not to be overlooked on account of its being familiar, since it would be as difficult to be explained as the most stupendous phaenomenon in nature." He then appended some verses on both the spring and autumn types:

> *Say, what impels, amidst surrounding snow,*
> *Congealed, the crocus' flamy bud to grow?*
> *Say, what retards, amidst the summer's blaze,*
> *Th' autumnal bulb till pale, declining days?*

The plant was described by Theophrastus, who noted that "the poison does not cause a speedy and easy death, but one that is lingering and slow." The ancient Egyptians, according to existing papyri, knew how to use the herb as a remedy for illnesses. And Dioscorides who, admitting that the bulb had a pleasant taste (others disagree), said that though "it killeth by choking," it could be used as a medicine in wise dosages. Nicander was somewhat less alarming, "But if a man taste the loathsome fire of Colchian Medea, the notorious Meadow-Saffron, an incurable itching assails his lips all over as he moistens them." Later accounts of its dread poisonous properties continued to echo Dioscorides. In his *New Herball* (sixteenth century) William Turner wrote, "It will strangell a man and kyll him in the space of one day, even as some kinde of Todestolles do." This was rephrased by Gerard, who was to a large extent translating Dodoens, and he added that those who eat "Medow Saffron must drinke the milke of a cow, or else death presently ensueth." I would suggest, however, that no one rely on such a simple antidote if he has eaten Colchicum.

The symptoms of poisoning were described by Culpeper: "A single grain only being swallowed by a person in health, by way of experiment, produced heat in the stomach, and soon after flushing heats in various parts of the body, with frequent shiverings, which were followed by colicky pains, after which an itching in the loins and urinary passages was perceived, and presently there came a continual inclination to make water, with a tremour, pain in the head, great thirst, a very quick pulse, and other disagreeable symptoms."

The toxic alkaloid which voices down the centuries have warned us about is called colchicine and is concentrated in the bulbs. It is one of the most extraordinary drugs known to man. Naturally, because of its associations with Medea of Colchis, the use, if not the understanding, of its powers passed on to later witches, sorcerers and wizards. It was mixed into cosmetic ointments—to cure pimples, for instance—and was an ingredient of many a love philtre. Medieval herb doctors prescribed it, quite properly as we know today, for gout and rheumatism. Culpeper, in his day, said it gave "the most astonishing success in dropsies and tertian agues." Then too, the ancient Egyptians had used it for gout and in Nero's day Dioscorides had called it a remedy for cancer and, with some limitations, he too was right.

Today the autumn crocus and its poison are under intense scrutiny by various branches of applied science. Some of the old folk remedies (not to mention murder by poison) have proved, as I have indicated, to be correct. Colchicine from autumn crocus is, in modern science, a specific for treatment of gout. And it is used in treating a kind of cancer—granulocytic leukemia. In connection with therapeutic application of the drug for man, perhaps some of the challenge of its possibilities is suggested by its present use by horticulturists and breeders of new varieties of plants. Colchicine is the only known substance which can "interfere with the process of cell division" and thus cause hereditary change in plants to produce mutants. Frankly, to me the implications are frightening and positively science-fiction, and I'm glad I have never tasted of Colchicum.

However, I am always delighted to taste the true crocus—at least, of its pistils. For that is what saffron is— the stigmas of the crocus pistils, which have been dried and used as flavoring, dye, scent and even medicine from the time of the Egyptians and Hippocrates to the present. This plant, also a native of Greece and Asia Minor but no longer found wild, has trumpet-shaped flowers shading from white to lilac, in which grow the three stamens with gold-orange anthers and a prominent red style below the stigma of the pistil. It takes about 75,000 flowers to produce a pound of saffron, roughly 4000 for one ounce. So think of this if you think the price of saffron is high; or if you get it cheap, realize it is probably not true saffron but safflower, that is, more coloring than flavoring.

Since it opens only in sunshine, the crocus is, naturally enough, dedicated to the sun. The legend holds that the plant was named after a Greek youth, Krokos, who pined away for love of Smilax, a shepherdess, but I have not been able to track down any source in Greek literature. Homer wrote that it was one of the flowers in the bed of Zeus and Hera and, with such a benediction, to say nothing of the natural virtues and delights of saffron, the plant became highly desirable to the elite and rich. Greeks and Romans scattered it by the basket-loads around their banquets and celebrations, scenting their wine and food with its aromatic but pungent flavor. In his cookery book Apicius set down the recipe for preparing Roman vermouth: "take 1 oz. cleaned and pounded Pontian wormwood, 1 date, 6 scruples each of mastic, bay and costmary, 3 scruples of saffron, 18 pints of the proper kind of wine. As it should be bitter, you need not add coal." They also used it, as a choice dye equal to Tyrian purple, to color their garments and even as a cosmetic.

In medieval times it was a component of electuaries and was an ingredient, along with aloes, antimony, ambergris and sugar, of one of Paracelsus' laudanums. An alchemist's recipe advises: "Take of the red and odorous hairs of the young lad whose blood is shed on the fields of mercury. . . ." But this metaphorical description of crocus does not sound like our Greek lad love-sick for Smilax; is there another legend as well? For ages ladies had used saffron to dye their hair but Henry I of England prohibited this waste of his favorite spice; yet the ladies were still using it in the sixteenth century to transform themselves into blondes. One might say, only their herb-purveyor knew!

Because only gods or kings could afford such an expensive spice or dye it became in the Orient, as in

Greece, a symbol of beauty and perfection. This tradition is reflected, perhaps, in the color of the robes of Buddhist monks. Medicinal virtues were also attributed to it in the Orient just as in England. Gerard considered saffron beneficial to the heart and the head for it "maketh the sences more quick and lively, shaketh off heavy and drowsie sleep, and maketh a man merry." He called it a special remedy "for those that have consumption of the lungs, and are, as we terme it, at deaths doore, and almost past breathing." But most of us today, I think, will value it, thanks to the Moors, for such dishes as saffron rice and paella.

As I have noted, if the saffron you buy has little flavor, it may be adulterated with, or be simply nothing but, the stamens of safflower (*Carthamus tinctorius*), one of the thistle-like members of the composite family. It is a native of the East Indies, an annual which grows to about three feet, producing large, bright orange flowers, and has long been cultivated as an ornamental as well as a source of food. The Romans used it in their foods, as can be seen in these two recipes which are inexplicit as to amounts, from Apicius:

> Hot sauce for roast boar: *Pepper, grilled cumin, celery-seed, mint, thyme, savory, safflower, toasted pine nuts or toasted almonds, honey, wine, condiment, vinegar, and a little oil.*

> Sauce for meat slices: *Pepper, celery-seed, caraway, savory, safflower, Welsh onion, toasted almonds, Jericho dates, condiment, oil, a little mustard.*

The leaves of safflower can be used to curdle milk, if that is what you need, and the seeds can be substituted for rennet in making cheese. Oil from the seeds has long been used in India for burning and for cooking. It has come into prominence in this country in recent years as a favorite oil of health-food faddists and cholesterol-watchers, and can be found bottled on the shelves of most grocery stores. In folk medicine an infusion of the flowers is prescribed for children's complaints, such as measles, fevers and skin eruptions, and it has also been recommended for jaundice and rheumatism. And if you should be living in Malaya and are seized with a "demoniacal possession," you will get a dose of it. Aside from the value of safflower as food and tonic, the flowers are an important source of yellow and red dyes for fabrics and cosmetics.

# Black Locust Tree

## Robinia pseudoacacia

*W*hen Matthew in the Bible related of John the Baptist that "his meat was locusts and wild honey," he did not mean that the holy man ate insects or the fruit of the tree we call locust. The translators for King James may not have been familiar with the carob (*Ceratonia siliqua*), a tree of the Mediterranean regions, or may have substituted the name of a similar pod-bearing tree known to Englishmen. The carob, of which John ate, bears long pods, as a locust does, but the carob pods are filled not with dry seeds but seeds surrounded by a sweet edible pulp.

Two of our authorities on edible wild plants, Fernald and Kinsey, report, with considerable trepidation and cautionary advice, that the flowers of the locust tree may be cooked and eaten. Another authority, Gibbons, with his usual enthusiasm, includes a recipe for batter with which to convert the blossoms into fritters. There is considerable disagreement over the danger of the locust in one or another of its parts; one writer early in this century recommended the inner bark as an emergency food for woodsmen. Still, it was this same cambium (inner bark or tissue) which poisoned the thirty-two orphans in a

Brooklyn institution, a case which is referred to in the introduction. A century ago an Englishman stated that the bark and roots had a sweet taste somewhat like licorice. Perhaps that taste was what attracted the orphans.

Regardless of the sweet taste of the roots, the flowers do indeed have a sweet scent and a charming effect. Mrs. Trollope, the mother of the English novelist, observed the tree while visiting in Maryland in 1830 and wrote: "The acacia, or as it is there called, the locust, blooms with great richness and profusion; I have gathered a branch less than a foot long, and counted twelve full bunches of flowers on it. The scent is equal to the orange flower." Any Southerner not even as old as I am must harbor fond memories of driving along an empty road lined on both sides for many yards with blooming locust trees, with the fragrant white clusters hanging among the delicate lacy green foliage. Even in an early model automobile, you could almost hear the buzzing of the swarming bees. It would be difficult to find such a road today, but Willa Cather has set it down for posterity:

> *Along the rail fences the locust trees were in bloom. The breeze caught their perfume and wafted it down the road. Every Virginian remembers those locusts which grow along the highways: their cloud-shaped masses of blue-green foliage and heavy drooping clusters of cream-white flowers like pea blossoms.*

And a poet has written:

> *In the red ravine, locust-tree roof*
> *And a million minute chandeliers of white*
> *Censing the air in spring.*

The tree has many thorns along the newer branches. A second trouble, of greater concern to parents, is that most parts of the tree appear to contain amounts of various toxic compounds which, when consumed, have killed animals and seriously disturbed human beings. Mrs. Leyel says that the poison "coagulates the casein of milk and clots the red corpuscles of certain animals." Which animals? On the death list, there are cattle, sheep, horses, mules; on the sick list, chickens and children.

The *Robinia*, or black locust, is native to the whole eastern and southern area of this country from Pennsylvania to the Ozarks. Because it is an extremely tenacious hardwood, it has been promoted into a sort of "crop" plant to take the place of the almost vanished chestnut as a source of fence posts, etc. It is said that some of the first houses built in Boston contained locust wood. Its characteristic vigor and resistance have caused it to be favored by large cities for street planting since it is a tree which can flourish despite poor soil, scant rainfall and ample fall of acid soot and grime. I have never seen one of these city immigrants bloom, but if they do, eventually those possibly dangerous pods will be falling off to tempt children.

There is a locust with pink flowers (*Robinia viscosa*), which has the repellent designation of "clammy locust" because of the sticky stems of leaves and flowers. Though a native of the South, it is often used as an ornamental in the North, where it adapts easily. The yellow-flowered honey locust (*Gleditschia triacanthos*), whose pulp in the ripe pods is reported to be sweet and harmless, is also being used as a tree for unhealthful cities. The horticulturists have been able to breed out its natural inclination to produce thorns and seeds—a floral *castrato*?

No matter about thorns or the color of its blossoms, if it is a locust, a *Robinia*, be careful about eating any part of it.

# Bleeding Heart

## Dicentra species

$F$rom my childhood, when the metaphors of plant names—snowdrop, maidenhair fern, Johnny-jump-up, elephant's-ear, Jack-in-the-pulpit—projected specific images which later materialized in the physical appearance of the flower, I have always had an affection for bleeding heart, even when the plant fell into neglect some decades ago. Maybe the name was too descriptive of the flower and that, like such scenic names as "Lover's Leap," "Rainbow Arch," "Mirror Lake," "Bridal Veil Falls," set it beyond the pale for sophisticates, who, after all, would have little truck with such poeticizing as a "bleeding heart." Certainly its neglect, which has now been largely overcome by virtue of its sheer lovely delicacy and the new varieties being developed, was not because anyone knew it contained poisons.

Some of this perennial's other descriptive names are Dutchman's-breeches and golden ear-drops, both in the yellow scale of colors; and paying tribute to the small tubers underground, squirrel-corn and turkey-corn. Another name for one variety, stagger weed, has no agreeable connotations and refers to the effect of that plant on cattle which feed heartily on it and its tubers. From those tubers grow up, depending on the species, fronds of feathery leaves eight inches to two feet high, and stalks bearing racemes or panicles of flowers. These flowers, again depending on the species, are organized into two pairs of petals, often united, which give the shape of the bleeding heart—two petals enclosing the stigma and hanging out, "bleeding," from the outer two which form a heart—or which, by a protuberance of the upper lobes of the outer petals, produces the upside-down shape of the Dutchman's-breeches. Other varieties are modifications of these, tending mostly toward the heart shape or even becoming somewhat bell-shaped. It is the curious variation of Dutchman's-breeches which has brought special notice to this rare woodland plant.

Of all the *Dicentrae*, Dutchman's-breeches is the most poisonous but the most difficult to capture in a garden. It is a native of the eastern United States, growing in the leaf mold of forests, a shy, low, retiring herb which resists transplanting. If you have one (*D. cucullaria*) in your garden, leave it alone. Don't move it, but don't eat it or let your children eat it. When moved from its original home, it usually never recovers. The flowers of this delightful plant are white, pale yellow, or white with yellowish lips on the petals. As in most plants of this genus, the flower stalks are faintly claret-colored.

Other varieties, especially those sold for gardens, have the usual heart-shaped pink, rose or red flowers with the drop of "blood" hanging from the point of the heart. They are not so averse to transplanting as Dutchman's-breeches.

Although the cultivated varieties are not so toxic as the wild ones, of which there are many from coast to coast, it is well to know that all the varieties are rather crowded with poisons. Six alkaloids have been found in *D. eximia*, the popular garden type. One of these poisons is very close to the drug in the poppy, but all of them have a narcotic effect. Livestock have died from eating the wild bleeding hearts, especially in the early spring.

It is of course applied by herbalists to certain complaints—skin troubles, scrofula and syphilis. The Chinese use one species in medicine; the Japanese use another for dysentery. In England it seems to be considered much the same as its kinsman, *Corydalis*. Some of these herbs have been found to have not merely six, but ten alkaloids in their foliage and roots. In any case, both *Dicentra* and *Corydalis* belong to the fumitory family, all of which contain some degree of poison. We have several varieties of wild *Corydalis* in this country, which poison grazing stock, and at least one rather delicate wild climbing fumitory (*Adlumia fungosa*) with pink flowers faintly resembling the bleeding heart. This may be quite like the fumitory which Cordelia, in *King Lear*, is told decorates her father out in the fields:

> *Crown'd with ranke femiter and furrow weeds,*
> *With hor-docks, hemlocke, nettles, cuckoo flowres.*

Fumitory has been recommended by herbalists for countless ailments—almost as many as there are species of the plant around the globe. Its toxic substance is similar to some of those in various members of the genera *Corydalis* and *Dicentra*.

Though cattle have died from grazing on wild bleeding hearts, there is no record of human death from eating any of the plants. They seem to be most toxic in the spring, and the garden types seem to be the least toxic of any. However, when it is known that a plant may contain a half dozen different alkaloids, I, for one, am not going to devour any of it.

# Box

*Buxus sempervirens*

*L*ike so many favorite hedge plants, box is both ever-green and poisonous. Since its growth is maddeningly slow, anyone who wishes to develop a boxwood hedge of any noticeable height will have to start early. I know of people in the South too advanced in years to dream of raising even a five-foot hedge but affluent enough to make their dreams come true, who have spent hundreds of dollars per shrub for the purchase and transplanting of century-old specimens. For the people of the South, ladies and lady-gardeners, especially, have a particular fancy for box.

Perhaps it is an inherited affinity or a symbol. The plant is not native to the United States but was introduced in colonial times from England by the settlers who longed for this reminder of their homeland. As a result, we have some handsome old box hedges as adjuncts to the great houses which still exist to our day along the Atlantic watershed from Virginia southward and across the interior to the settlements along the Mississippi River to New Orleans. This variety of box was not hardy enough for the northern climates, where oriental varieties were even-tually found to be more adaptable.

*Box* *(23)*

One has only to look at a well-tended hedge or topiary to understand part of the attraction of the plant. The twiggy growth inside is dense and tangled, impenetrable except by snakes, insects and the smallest animals; the outside is a compact sheath of tiny, glossy, dark green leaves. Some writers have objected to the odor of the plant as somewhat fox-like, and one says the smell and the bitter taste prevent most animals from being poisoned by it. For myself, having strolled on a sunny summer day through extensive alleys of towering box hedge, interspersed with French neo-classical statues, near St. Francisville, Louisiana, I can only say the odor struck me as a delicate agreeable pungency, quite compatible with aromatic crape myrtles and cedars, and a sharp relief from the sweetness of roses and cape jasmines.

In Europe the box grows into a fifteen-foot tree and has thus been a source of wood. The Greeks, who had dedicated the tree to Pluto, lord of Hades and the dead, and the Romans both prized the wood—compact, fine-grained and hard—for making musical instruments. It is said that the clipping of box into hedges originated in the time of Julius Caesar. By the time of Martial, a century later, the trimmed hedge was a status symbol, as can be inferred from his description of a poor man's country house:

> . . . *no boxe-hedges there*
> *Cut into various figures doe appeare*
> *To please the eye. . .*

The flowers of box, which grow in small clusters, are of a sickly yellowish hue, and produce seed capsules, each containing three seeds. The leaves, which contain the poison, buxine, were once used medicinally to treat fevers; the drug is known to affect the nervous system and to be emetic, purgative and narcotic. Despite the repellent odor and taste, grazing animals, even pigs, are known to have eaten the clippings from box hedges and died from doing so.

A more pleasant result of using box leaves externally has been reported: a decoction of the leaves will not only stimulate the growth of hair but will give a lovely chestnut color to gray hair. But surely that couldn't be the reason all the Southern ladies wanted to have box in their gardens?

# Castor Bean Plant

## Ricinus communis

*A*nyone who, in his childhood, was forced to swallow that sovereign remedy of the early part of this century, castor oil, will need no persuasion to agree that it is, on the basis of taste at least, a virulent poison. But tastes differ greatly with individuals and with habits, and though the castor bean plant was given by the Egyptians and the Hebrews a name which means roughly "nauseous to the taste," there is testimony that the Javanese cook the young leaves and flowers and even the seeds for food. I remember that in my childhood, when I was closest to the sickening viscous oil, I was appalled at a man who frequently worked for my parents and had an abiding appetite for castor oil. My mother saved the remnants in bottle after bottle for him and I have watched him drain six or seven at a time with great satisfaction. In spite of what we may think, the oil extracted from the beans is not poisonous, for cooking and processing destroy the poison, but the raw beans and all other parts of the plant are indeed full of a powerful poison.

The poison is a phytotoxin called ricin, which affects the blood. Its highest concentration is in the seeds, one of which, if chewed and swallowed, could kill a child; if a

*Ricinus communis*

large number should be eaten, collapse of even an adult might follow almost immediately. Because the seeds are small and glossy—black or mottled with gray or brown— they are attractive to young children, who may eat them with no thought of taste.

A native of Africa and a member of the spurge family, the castor bean plant, because it grows easily, swiftly and provides quick foliage in barren areas and because its oil has commercial and medicinal uses, has been widely transplanted over the world. It is an annual in this country but in the South it grows as high as six or eight feet in a summer, and in the tropics even to thirty or forty feet. Its attraction lies in the foliage rather than in the insignificant flowers, which are male or female, but are produced on the same plant. The leaves are impressively broad, either green, often touched with bronze, or dull mulberry in color. In fact, the plant is such a space-filler in gardens that flower catalogues instruct the gardening enthusiast, not to beware of the poison, but to allow three to four feet between plants.

It is appropriate that such a rampant-growing herb should be the one chosen by God—referred to as a gourd in the Bible—to shelter Jonah: "And the Lord God prepared a gourd, and made it come up over Jonah, that it might be a shadow over his head, to deliver him from his grief. So Jonah was exceeding glad of the gourd."

The seeds are formed in soft burry capsules, three seeds in each, and the oil is extracted by pressing and treating them to remove the ricin. In Europe the oil is usually "cold drawn"—pressed out without heat applied. In the United States the seeds are dry-roasted an hour or so, the oil is then pressed out, mixed with water and boiled to purify it of extraneous substances. The "press cakes" of seeds which are left are used, sometimes with ill effects, as livestock food in winter. The oil itself has many uses, aside from the gruesome medicinal one of a once popular purgative; in ancient times it served as lamp oil and today it is often used as a lubricant in industrial plants.

Herodotus, in *The Persian Wars*, reported that "the Egyptians who live in the marshes use for the anointing of their bodies an oil made from the castor berry." He notes that the plants grow wild in Greece and the liquid obtained from the seeds "is found to be unctuous, and as well suited as olive-oil for lamps, only that it gives out an unpleasant odour." Could castor oil, rather than inferior olive oil, be the stuff Juvenal was referring to in his *Satire V* as a salad dressing, but which smelled of lamp oil and was imported from Numidia?

> *. . . such vile stuff that no one in Rome would dare*
> *To go into the baths if an African king were*
> *    there—*
> *It will even keep you safe from snakebites any-*
> *    where.*[1]

Dioscorides and Pliny knew castor oil as a violent purgative. The latter wrote of it: "It is good also for diseases of the joints, for all indurations, for the uterus, the ears and burns; with the ashes moreover of the murex shell for inflammation of the anus, and likewise for the itch. It improves the complexion, and through its fertilizing power it promotes the growth of hair. The seed from which it is made no living creature will touch."

The castor bean also had the power of a magical charm, as we learn from Pseudo-Apuleius, whose book on herbs was translated into Anglo-Saxon in the eleventh century and was extremely popular.

> *For hail and rough weather, to turn them away, if*
> *thou havest in thy possession this wort, which is*

---

[1] *The Satires of Juvenal*, trans. by Hubert Creekmore (A Mentor Book; New York, The New American Library of World Literature Inc., 1963).

*named ricinus, and* which is not a native of England, *or if thou hangest some seed of it in thine house, or have it or its seed in any place whatsoever, it turneth away the tempestuousness of hail, and if thou hangest its seed on a ship, to that degree wonderful it is, that it smootheth every tempest. This wort thou dost take thus speaking, Herba ricinus, precor . . . te iussit nasci: that is, in our language Wort ricinus, I pray that thou be at mine songs, and that thou turn away hails and lightning bolts, and all tempests, through the name of Almighty God, who hight thee to be produced; and thou shalt be clean when thou pluckest this herb.*

Here are some extracts from a letter of 1921 quoted in Grieve and Leyel's *A Modern Herbal:* "I told him they were Castor Oil seeds. He said 'I think it would be a good idea to make an emulsion of these and take it instead of the oil.' I told him to shell them first, as there was a poisonous principle under the shell. He did so. I do not think he used more than six of the seeds, and when he had made the emulsion, which looked very nice, he drank it all. Within ten minutes he disappeared out of the shop unexpectedly, and an hour or two afterwards someone went up to his bedroom and found him lying there unconscious. . . . After medical treatment, he lay for nearly a fortnight before he was able to resume work, and during that time he scarcely took any food. . . . I guess it—the emulsion—had acted very much in the same way as a few drops of croton oil would have done had it been made into an emulsion—as an irritant poison."

# Cherry Laurel

## Prunus caroliniana

*T*his lovely, shiny-leaved tree is not a true laurel at all, but a wild cherry, a member of the genus *Prunus* of the rose family. From *Prunus* we derive our word prune, for the dried plum, but the word for the fresh plum comes from Old English *plūme*. The genus comprises not only plums, but cherries, peaches, and apricots and the flowering almond. The interrelationship can be suggested to your nose if you crush leaves or twigs from a wild cherry tree, enclose them in a jelly jar and keep the jar warm for a few minutes. On opening it you will smell bitter almonds, which is the characteristic odor of the glycocide, amygdalin, which contains hydrocyanic (prussic) acid.

This poison is often fatal to stock on overgrazed or drought-parched ranges when cherry leaves may be browsed out of desperation. It is contained in the leaves, the bark and the kernels of the fruit stones of most wild cherry trees. The cherry laurel is a favorite plant for gardens, because it grows fast and is evergreen in temperate climates. The other wild cherries, with such descriptive praenomens as black, choke, fire, rum, bird, pin, and sand, and wild plums such as beach plum and wild-goose plum, are valued for their fruits which are edible, though bitter,

*Prunus serotina*

when cooked and can be made into jams, jellies and pies.

Though the conditions of poisoning will vary, and some people have eaten some of these wild fruits raw without ill effects, the wise man will be wary of them and think of cyanide.

The species *caroliniana* is indigenous to the south-eastern regions of America where it often grows higher than forty feet and flowers in axillary racemes of tiny blossoms, creamy-white with a brownish calyx, which develop into small shiny fruits. The European cherry laurel

(*P. Laurocerasus*), whose habitat is southeastern Europe to Iran, has been widely introduced as an ornamental shrub in European countries. It is very similar to the American species, but it seldom grows into even a small tree. Centuries ago uses were found for the toxic substances in the leaves, and in time cherry laurel water was distilled from them, as "waters" were, and still are, distilled from many other plants.

The recipe for cherry laurel water in the British pharmacy goes thus: "One pound of fresh leaves of cherry-laurel, 2½ pints of water. Chop the leaves, crush them in a mortar, and macerate them in the water for 24 hours; then distil 1 pint of liquid; shake the product, filter through paper, and preserve it in a stoppered bottle."

Four drams of such water, along with crushed bitter almonds and other ingredients, were mixed to produce a face lotion offered by the famous "beautician," Thomas Goulard, to the ladies of eighteenth century Paris. And in the latter part of that same century, in 1780, a poison which was probably the same kind of water figures in a famous murder case. I say "probably" because no one involved in the trial was more specific in identifying the fluid than as "laurel water."

The situation was this: Captain John Donellan, a man with the conventional tastes of his times for high living, wenching and gambling, found himself, a cashiered officer, in desperate need of an income and wished to marry the daughter of the wealthy Lady Boughton. Under the disgrace of his discharge from the army, he could not win the approval of the girl's mother, so he persuaded Miss Boughton to elope with him. Lady Boughton cut off her daughter's resources, but at length a reconciliation brought the young couple to her country estate where her son lived, Sir Theodosius, who, since the age of seventeen, had suffered from the "pox" and was taking medicines for it. Sir Theodosius was then twenty and, at his majority within a few months, he would come into an annual income of two thousand pounds. If he died a minor, this money would go to his sister, Mrs. Donellan.

On the fatal morning, though the new "physic" sent by the pharmacist had smelled of bitter almonds and tasted nauseating, Lady Boughton gave him a dose. In the *Newgate Calendar* the scene is described:[1] "Two minutes after Sir Theodosius had taken the draught he struggled very much. . . . He made a prodigious rattling in his stomach, and guggling; and these symptoms continued about ten minutes. He then seemed as if he were going to sleep, or inclined to doze." His mother left the room for a few minutes and returned to find him "with his eyes fixed upwards, his teeth clenched, and foam running out of his mouth."

These details, we learn from William Roughead,[2] are almost direct testimony from Lady Boughton at the trial, for such was the interest in the case that two separate transcripts were made in shorthand and later published. The many points at issue—the two bottles of medicine, Donellan's disposing of their contents and washing the bottles, his possession of a still, the presence of laurel bushes in the garden—are too complex to go into here. Dr. Rattray testified that the poison was, in his opinion, laurel water.

But from what *kind* of laurel? It would not be *Daphne laureola*, which would cause vomiting and purging. Bay laurel (*Laurus nobilis*) would excite rather than depress and bring sleep. Cherry laurel, it seems to me, is the best guess, for it contains prussic acid—cyanide—whose sedative effects and later manifestations are very much like those of Sir Theodosius Boughton. Whatever it

[1] *The Complete Newgate Calendar,* 4 vols. (London, The Navarre Society, 1926), vol. 4, pp. 148–153.

[2] William Roughead, *Reprobates Reviewed* (London, Cassell & Company Ltd., 1941), pp. 109–137.

was, Captain Donellan paid the penalty for it and was executed on April 2, 1781, after writing a denunciation of his mother-in-law as the culprit and expressing a hope that all good men might be spared such relatives.

This case, perhaps because of the unusual fact of the existence of two transcripts of the trial, has aroused much interest in later times among attorneys, criminologists, toxicologists and even novelists. In 1849 the prolific writer G. P. R. James published a three-decker Victorian novel defending Donellan as a victim of circumstantial evidence, under the scarcely veiled title of *Sir Theodore Broughton: or Laurel Water.*

# Chinaberry Tree

## Melia Azedarach

Since it has so many attractive qualities one must
wonder why the chinaberry tree is not more highly
esteemed in this country. It was pretty enough in our
ancestors' eyes to move them to introduce the tree from
its native Syria, Iran, India and other Asian lands as an
ornamental for their gardens. Two of its less familiar
names are Indian-lilac and Pride of India and, because
of the family to which it belongs, it is sometimes spoken
of as mahogany.

The tree grows to a moderate height, thirty to forty-
five feet, and its spreading branches provide a cool shade,
a shade whose freshness, in my recollection, seems to have
been intensified by the denseness of the foliage against a
hot southern sun and a sort of crispness in the air, as if a
faint redolent moisture exuded from the warm, quivering
leaves. These light green leaves are pinnate and compound, with stems which spring oppositely along the central stem in imitation of the entire form—a form rather
like the fronds of certain ferns, bracken or maidenhair.
The purple or lilac flower is made up of five or six petals,
opened flat, and from the center of the flower a tube
rises, usually paler in color, into which the stamens are

*Melia Azedarach*

fused; the open end of the tube looks like stiff fringe or fine scalloping and is slightly darker than the rest of the flower. The blossoms hang in many-branched panicles and at maturity become green, then yellow, drupes—or berries.

The fragrance of the blooms is heavy, insistent and to some people almost overpowering, especially on a hot day. It may be this characteristic of the chinaberry that put it out of favor with sensitive gardeners. Or it might be because the dense shade usually prevents grass from growing around the trunk. Or that the berries fall and mess up the ground with their decaying pulp, or that the tree, being deciduous, covers the earth with small yellow leaves in the autumn. Whatever the bill of particulars which condemned the tree to the edges of limbo, I know that when I was growing up it was to be found most frequently in the yards of the lower classes, and was spoken of in rather contemptuous tones, often including a derogatory "old" as the adjective.

Thus, from what must have once been a high station similar to that of cattleyas and bromeliads today, it was relegated to the company of cockscombs and periwinkle and others in the nether status of horticulture. But cockscombs, through the ministrations of hybridizers, have made a comeback. Perhaps the "bad" qualities, including its poison, can be bred out of the chinaberry. Meanwhile, perhaps in disgust at its lack of favor, the tree has reverted to the wilds in many regions where it was introduced. Apparently it cannot survive the severe winters of the North and West, but it has accommodated itself handsomely to the mild weather of the American South, Mexico, Africa and the West Indies.

In my boyhood we used to gather the ripe yellow berries and boil them in a tin can—probably a lard container—until the pulp had dissolved and seeped through the hulls. The smell was rather unpleasant and makes me think that Fernald and Kinsey were correct in stating that no one who had tasted the drupes would be "apt to do it again." After thorough boiling, the berries, with the outer shells shrunken in between the ridges of the seeds, were an ugly pale fawn color, but when dried they could be dyed drab red, yellow, blue, purple and green and strung as beads. We imagined we were practicing some ancient craft of the Choctaws and Cherokees and didn't know the chinaberry arrived after most of those peoples had left on a forced journey to the West.

Those berries—drupes—the flowers which produce

them, and the rough bark contain poison which has stricken children, chickens, pigs and other animals. The symptoms are irregular breathing with a feeling of suffocation, and paralysis.

# *Christmas Rose*

## *Helleborus niger*

*C*hristmas . . . rose . . . two words replete with lovely associations. And as if that were not enough and they were still worried about the appeal of the plant, copywriters for nurserymen's catalogues have put forth a "legend" which claims that the flower sprang from the tears of a shepherd girl who had no gift for the Christ child. Leaving aside the obvious plagiarism of pagan myths, one can only feel the concept highly inappropriate for a plant known to be poisonous from long before the time of Jesus.

The application of "Christmas" to this flower seems to have begun in the seventeenth century. Gerard notes that it "floureth about Christmasse" and adds later on, "In high Dutch it is called Christs herbe, and that because it floureth about the birth of our Lord Jesus Christ." Culpeper says it is called "setter-wort, setter-grass, Bear's-foot, Christmas herb, and Christmas-flower." To prior sources it was simply hellebore and it has a long history of citations as a drug.

Hippocrates included it in his works and Theophrastus wrote that it was fatal to horses, oxen and pigs, but was useful as a purge. Horace and Juvenal, among others, refer to it as a cure for insanity. Nicander gave it as a remedy for poisonous bites. It was prescribed by Dioscorides as "good for ye Epileptical, Melancholicall, Frantic, Arthriticall, Paralyticall." In *Le Menagier de Paris,* written during the Middle Ages, a recipe for balls of paste used for killing wolves and foxes included black hellebore. In writing his work on gardening and farming, Columella directed the prospective agriculturist to choose a plot of ground:

> *That bears no hellebore with noxious juice,*
> *Nor suffers yews to grow, nor poisons strong*
> *Exudes, though it may bear the maddening flower*
> *Of the half-human mandrake, hemlock drear. . . .*

The plant figures in the purgative remedies which Chaucer wrote out for Chanticleer's wife to address to her husband in the Nun's Priest's tale. A cure for melancholy listed by Michael Drayton in his *Polyolbion* is "soveraign hellebore" and Robert Burton in his *Anatomy of Melancholy* bears him out:

> *Borage and hellebore fill two scenes,*
> *Sovereign plants to purge the veins*
> *Of melancholy, and cheer the heart*
> *Of those black fumes which make it smart.*

Black hellebore was also a favorite of witches, says Dorothy Jacob, and therefore has "a surprisingly bad name." According to her, it was used in many charms, "partly because one of the fingers of its bifurcated leaves is evil. *But only a witch knows which!"* Where, then, does this leave that sad little shepherdess and her tears?

The catalogue of references might be extended for pages, for black hellebore is one of the four most ancient poisons, the other three being aconite, hemlock and nightshade. Black hellebore (one cannot always be certain, in the older writers, just which species is meant) is a native of Europe and Asia, one of the buttercup family, and was introduced into this country as an ornamental herb treasured because of its large, midwinter-blooming white flowers and its evergreen foliage. It grows from one to two feet high; the "innocent" (as the catalogues say) white flowers, sometimes as broad as four inches across, at length take on a pink tinge and after a long time turn green; the leaves are deep green and leathery, "somewhat bluntly nicked or toothed, having sundry divisions or cuts," as Gerard puts it.

Christmas rose is the true hellebore (there are false ones, treated below) and its poisonous principle, as found in the roots and leaves, has not been definitely analyzed, though it is thought to be related to digitalis. Its European counterpart is *H. viridis* or *H. foetidus,* both having greenish flowers, in the former plant tinged at the edges with purple, in the latter with red; and naturally, considering its Latin description "foetidus," the latter has a bad odor. Gilbert White found these two species growing on the property at Selborne and in his *Natural History* of that place he described them; of this latter plant he wrote: "*Helleborus foetidus,* stinking hellebore, bear's foot, or setterworth, all over the High-wood and Coney-croft-hanger: this continues a great branching plant the winter through, blossoming about January, and is very ornamental in shady walks and shrubberies. The good women give the leaves powdered to children troubled with worms; but it is a violent remedy, and ought to be administered with caution." A more pertinent comment on this eighteenth century English medical practice appeared in a contemporary journal: "Where it killed not the patient, it would certainly kill the worms, but the worst of it is that it will sometimes kill both."

False hellebore (*Veratrum viride,* or in Europe *V. album*) is a plant of very different aspect, but of comparable toxic powers. It is said that Solon, centuries ago, used it in what may be the earliest application of what we might call "chemical warfare"; while besieging the city of Cirrheus, he dammed up the river, its water supply, steeped hellebore in it and released the water, so that the citizens, on drinking of the water, became so weakened by the resultant purging that they could not defend their city. The juice of this plant was used by the Celts and Gauls to poison arrows and in the same way, on the North American continent, by the Indians.

This false hellebore grows up like a cornstalk to a height of eight feet, with broad, heavily veined, cupping, pleated leaves and a spike of green or white flowers at the top. It is not a plant one would find in a flower garden, but a broad stand of them in their native habitat, damp woods or open lowlands, is a striking sight. One thinks of the dream tropics painted by the Douanier Rousseau. In its way the plant simply *looks* insidious; and, as if to live up to expectations, it contains not merely one, but several alkaloids, among them veratridine, jervine, cevadine and veratralbine. They affect the nervous system and through it the heart and the arteries, and the symptoms of poisoning they produce in any animal which eats the plants are all-inclusive and very distressing. Even more appalling is the effect on ewes—*if* they consume a certain Western species a day or so after impregnation. The lambs are born with incredible deformities; they may have a very short nose or none at all, and only one eye in the middle of the forehead, like Polyphemus.[1] We are aware that drugs can cause deformities in human fetuses as well; thalidomide was the recent, tragic example.

Yet, horrible as the effects of poisoning by false hellebore may be, the drugs in the plant, extracted and purified, are being used in medicine today for various cardiac disorders, and intensive investigation and study

---

[1] Kingsbury, *Deadly Harvest*, pp. 77–78.

of their useful potentialities are going on. *Veratrum viride* provides a powerful drug for reducing high blood pressure and is used with *Rauwolfia* as a hypotensive medicine of the tranquilizer type. It is said, in fact, that one great drug manufacturing company in the United States was "virtually founded" on these two plants.[2]

[2] Margaret B. Kreig, *Green Medicine. The Search for Plants That Heal* (New York, Rand McNally & Company, 1964), p. 326.

# Daphne

## Daphne mezereum; D. cneorum; D. laureola

*D*aphne was a beautiful Greek nymph, the daughter of Peneus, a river-god, and was a devotee of Athene. Naturally, as such behavior was traditional with the Greek gods, Apollo wanted to ravish her and, as she fled from him at Delphi, she prayed to Athene (the virgin goddess), who changed her into a laurel tree before Apollo could accomplish his purpose. As a result Apollo made the laurel tree sacred to him and, as god of music, poetry and prophecy, endowed it with the distinction of signifying artistic achievement. And so a wreath of laurel, or bay, to be more exact (and to relate to our culinary bay leaves), was awarded the winners in poetic, musical, and athletic competitions.

The confusion of plants was thus established even in legend—daphne, laurel, bay. Daphne's laurel (*D. laureola*) is not Apollo's laurel (*Laurus nobilis*), which is the tree from which we get our bay leaves; and the old words read "crowned with bay" when describing the contest winners. Nor are other laurels, such as cherry laurel,

*Daphne mezereum*

mountain laurel and so on, the same as the true laurel. Something got mixed up. For Apollo's *Laurus nobilis* is the one which his priestesses and votaries, and the pythoness of the oracles, chewed to give them the gift (or hallucination) of prophecy. *Daphne laureola*, of a completely different family, could hardly produce that narcotic effect.

A similarity of leaf shapes seems to have led to this tangle. For instance, Theophrastus called by the name "daphne" such dissimilar plants as true laurel, oleander and mangrove. Even Pliny, after a long consideration of the uses of bay laurel, adds, "Taken in drink in the same way, the wild bay, called daphnoides . . . is beneficial; three drachmae of the leaves, fresh or dried, taken with salt in hydromel, relax the bowels. Chewed this bay brings up phlegm and the leaves bring up vomit, being injurious to the stomach. In this way, too, the berries, fifteen at a time, are taken as a purge." He has nothing to say about the legend of Daphne and Apollo.

Maybe Robert Graves' approach in *The White Goddess* is the more valid: "The connection of poetry with laurel is not merely that laurel is an evergreen and thus an emblem of immortality: it is also an intoxicant. The female celebrants of the Triple Goddess [of the sky, the earth, the underworld] at Tempe had chewed laurel leaves to induce a poetic and erotic frenzy, as the Bacchanals chewed ivy—*daphne* may be a shortened form of *daphoine*, 'the bloody one,' a title of the Goddess." And he cites very appropriate lines from John Skelton's "Garland of Laurell" on the Triple Goddess:

> *Diana in the leavès green,*
> *Luna that so bright doth sheen,*
> *Persephone in Hell.*

But still and all, this does not lend substance to the story of Daphne and Apollo. It might be that the plant was always called daphne by the Greeks and the myth was invented to fit the fact. Or how much of the legend of the poet Daphnis (so often coupled with Chloe in later poetry) is mixed in the origin of the myth and the name of the plant?

Whatever the answer, few people, at least few in England, seem willing to call the plant daphne. A more common name for *D. mezereum* is mezereon, but Culpeper called it spurge olive; and *D. laureola* is called spurge laurel. The denotative "spurge" in these instances apparently springs from the origins of the common name of the genus *Euphorbia* from the Old French word meaning "to purge." For the juices of the *Daphne laureola* are, as Culpeper put it, "a rough purgative." Chaucer simply called the plant "laureole" when he included it among the laxatives prescribed in "The Nun's Priest's Tale." But this violent effect on the digestive tract, upper or lower, is produced by ingestion of any of the daphnes.

The best known of these plants in the United States, it may be, is the pretty, odorous, rosy-flowered *Daphne cneorum,* which decorates many rock gardens with its low cushions of bright color in the spring. While *D. cneorum* grows less than a foot high, the *Mezereum* species, on the other hand, reaches a height of four to five feet, with *Laureola* falling in between with a two to three foot growth. All of these were introduced into North America, where mezereon has also gone wild and may often be found on the rocky banks of abandoned limestone quarries. But there is a similar native American plant (*Dirca palustris*) which the English call "American Mezereon" or leatherwood (its American common name), which belongs to the same family as daphne.

The flowers of daphne are like tiny trumpets with the flare of the bell divided into four segments. In the rock garden species they appear in clusters like umbels at the ends of the branches. In the other daphnes the flowers emerge in clusters along the branches—in the case of *mezereum* before the leaves appear—and they are pink to purple, almost oppresively fragrant, producing red berries (though in some species the flower is white and forms a yellow berry) and in the evergreen *laureola* the flower, says Culpeper, is "of a sad, yellowish green colour, and unpleasant smell" and it matures into a purple-black berry.

All members of the *mezereum* group are toxic, and we understand little more says Kingsbury, than Dioscorides did except certain specific effects of its poisons. Linnaeus recorded the case of a girl who died after eating a dozen berries. And other similar reports have followed in the intervening years. Apparently adults can resist the poisons more readily than children. But we have little knowledge or understanding of its variables—the effects of seasonal, geographic, climatic or soil conditions—or of any sound remedy for the poison.

Even in recommending *laureola* for treatment of rheumatic fevers, dropsy and venereal disease, Culpeper felt compelled to add that it "requires some caution in the administration, and might, in unskilful hands, be productive of dangerous consequences." In our own age Mrs. Quelch is more direct, "The berries of both varieties have been included amongst rustic medicines, and many deaths are recorded in consequence."

The poisonous substance in the daphne is, so far as it has been analyzed, a glycoside called daphnin. It has been used in official medicine, and it is usually sold commercially in the form of stripped bark. The leaves and bark of *D. laureola* have also been used—unofficially—to induce abortion. The reputation of the plant and the elusive secret of its poison should keep anyone, even without a goddess's intervention, from violating Daphne.

# English Ivy

## Hedera Helix

*E*veryone must be familiar with the sight of stone or brick walls of homes, churches, universities and gardens shimmering with curtains of dark green English ivy leaves, even when blobs of snow cling to the network of vine and tendrils which support it; or with the lighter-hued Boston ivy, which in autumn turns red and gold before dropping its leaves to expose the walls. Only the English ivy concerns us here, since it, in all its parts, is poisonous; some allergic people react to it as most people do to poison ivy (*Rhus toxicodendron*).

Perhaps because of its hardiness, its beauty, its evergreen foliage and its habit of growth, Western literature and art is full of laudatory references to its virtues. It was sacred to gods of vegetation—the Phrygian Attis and the Egyptian Osiris, for example, both of whom were represented by evergreen trees—and was associated with the Greek Dionysus, or Bacchus, also a god of trees and, in particular, wine. Bacchus appears crowned with ivy leaves and his votaries, the Bacchantes, ate them to induce their excitement and intoxication. The ancient Homeric *Hymn VII* tells how Dionysus as a boy was kidnapped by

*Hedera Helix*

pirates, who realized too late that he was a god, and as their ship sailed away:

> *Then sprang a vine, with swaying clusters bent,*
> *This way and that in the square-sail top surround-*
> *ing;*
> *Dark ivy bloomed, and rich with berries clung*
> *About the mast; the tholes were garland-hung.*

This same passage is the background for a beautiful section of Ezra Pound's "Canto II," though Pound also relies on part of the *Metamorphoses* of Ovid. In his *Fasti* Ovid also deals with ivy and its relation to Bacchus; it is dear to Bacchus because when he was a baby and his stepmother, Juno, who hated him, went out searching for him, the nymphs of Nysa hid the cradle behind ivy leaves.

Theocritus, describing a wine cup, wrote, "About its lip winds ivy, ivy flecked with golden berries." Two centuries later Catullus described a band of Satyrs, who are natural associates of Bacchantes, as dancing "With frantic rout and bacchanalian roar. Their ivy-circled spears on high they bore."

These citations are the merest fraction of the extant literary references, which span the writings of over a thousand years. And they are concerned only with the religious, symbolic, beauteous nature of the plant. On the medicinal side we find that Hippocrates included it among his simples; Pseudo-Apuleius named it as a remedy for "water sickness" (dropsy); and Culpeper, always lavish in handing out cures, recommended it for jaundice, worms, the plague, "the lax and bloody-flux" and stated that it "breaks the stone, provokes urine and women's courses."

Ivy has always been supposed to possess magical virtues and is the subject of much superstition and folklore. A strand of it bound around the head would prevent intoxication—perhaps because poets' heads were wreathed with it in ancient times. A spray of it hung above a door signified a tavern and is probably the earliest tavern sign. Because it clings to walls and trees, it is a symbol of fidelity. There are many early ballads dealing with the ivy twining round the holly, but not in connection with their use as decorations during the Christmas season; holly and ivy were male and female symbols, established in the religious beliefs of forgotten ages. Many folk remedies call for the use of ivy and one, which persists to the present time and is vouched for by those in Ireland who have tried it, is ivy leaves soaked in vinegar for the relief of corns.

Though it is called English ivy, it is the same ivy which grows throughout Europe. That it is clinging is well known. Theophrastus considered it a parasite, "it is mischievous to plant this against any tree; for it destroys and starves any tree by withdrawing the moisture." Many people have denied this charge, but it seems to be at least semi-parasitic. Botanists say that the fibers by which it climbs a tree fasten into the crevices of the bark by flattening into discs at the end and thus eventually can become roots which draw nourishment from the host plant.

However, if you need nourishment, if you are hungry for greenery or berries, forget the literary, artistic and medicinal recommendations of ivy. Forget that the Bacchantes ate ivy leaves—after doing so, they tore Pentheus limb from limb. Forget that birds eat ivy berries with impunity—they also eat worms. Berries, leaves, stems and roots of ivy contain a glycoside called hederin which has poisoned animals and children. Moreover, it doesn't taste good. But are children aware of this—or do they care?

# Foxglove

## *Digitalis purpurea*

*T* hough the plant has a fascinating history, it is a short one, for foxglove was unknown or scarcely known to the ancient writers. It was described by Dioscorides in the first century but it had no Latin or Greek name. Because its habitat is the lands along the Atlantic seaboard of Europe, it was seldom if ever seen by the classical writers of the Mediterranean and Aegean civilizations, and certainly was not prescribed medicinally. Its Latin name, *Digitalis* (from *digitus*, "finger"), was bestowed upon it by Hieronymus Bock (Tragus) of Strassburg in 1539 and a few years later it was listed under that name by Leonhard Fuchs in his *De Historia Stirpium*.

The English name, foxglove, has its own curious background. Now we know that hardly any foxes have ever worn gloves; obviously this designation is not truly descriptive, and yet a legend from northern Europe has it that bad fairies gave the fox the blossoms to slip over his toes and thus muffle his approach to the chicken roosts. The German name, *fingerhut*, "thimble," is at least reasonably apt and is repeated in an English folk name, fairy thimbles. Other obvious images, which bear connotations of menace, are the Scottish dead men's bells and the En-

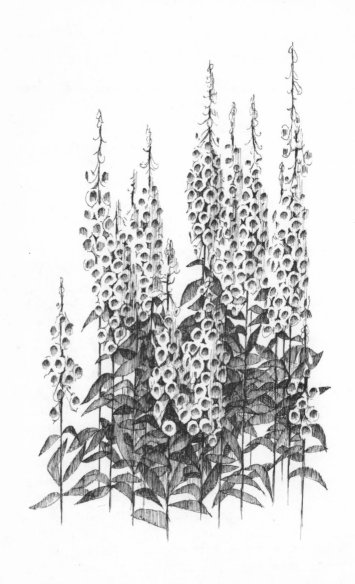

*Digitalis purpurea*

glish bloody fingers. Next we come to the gloves for fingers —gloves of Our Lady (a translation of the French *gants de Notre-Dame*) and Virgin's glove. At the opposite end of the scale we find, again with the implication of evil and a suggestion of the drugs hidden in the plant, witches' gloves; then, from Wales, goblin's gloves, from England, fairy's gloves, and at last, harking back to a distant time, folk's gloves.

Why folk's gloves? Why, of course, for the "folk," the "good folk," the "little people" who have kept turning up in the names cited above—the fairies. And, if we are to credit other names given the plant, the fairies used the blossom also as petticoats, caps and bells, to say nothing of the fact that they often hid inside the fat roomy corolla, as one can observe insects at sundown taking refuge in them from the night's cold and from dewfall or possible rain. But if you should inconsiderately jostle the blossoms, you might receive a stroke from the fairy's wand, with dire results. Who can say how many gnats, flies and mosquitoes have crowded in on fairies sheltering inside foxglove blooms, and now no longer vex the human race, or, on the other hand, how many hives have produced a meager harvest of honey because of discommoded bees? For bees love the foxglove and swarm to it, but not because it is, as it always has been, a truly magical herb. Another tale is that when the wind shakes the bell-flowers they make music which only fairies can hear.

It was a favorite of the Druids because it flowered at the time of their midsummer sacrifice. But we have no evidence that they or any of the early sixteenth century herbalists were aware of the genuine magical properties lurking in the herb. It is said that the Welsh, for some reason, had a particular fancy for comparing the flower to blushing beauty in young girls. *The Mabinogion* describes the maiden Olwen, who became Kilhwch's bride, thus, "Her two breasts were more white than the breast of a white swan; her cheeks more red than the foxglove." In the beautiful, moving "Lament for Lucy Lloyd," Llyweln Goch wrote, "Come, with your cheeks of foxgloves, Up from the earth's dreary house."[1]

In a later day it was only the colleagues of the fairies, those potion brewers the witches, who seemed to know something of what the foxglove could do for the human body. But because they kept their counsel, and because the plant for some reason had been so little popularized, it was almost never mentioned in the Elizabethan poets' works. Even at the end of the sixteenth century, Gerard was to write, "The Fox-gloves in that they are bitter, are hot and dry, with a certaine kinde of clensing qualitie joyned therewith; yet are they of no use, neither have they any place amongst medicines, according to the Antients."

Let us not blame Gerard too much—he was to a large extent translating Dodoens, a Belgian herbalist of the earlier part of the era, and had made no effort to test the potentials of the plant. If "the Antients" had said it was of no use, there was the answer for his generation of scientists. The brewers of potions and magic philtres, however, were not idle, once the herb came to their attention. It was put into ointments and mixtures prescribed for everything "from colds to epilepsy," but almost never for the diseases for which it is today a specific and mysteriously effective remedy.

The foxglove, in fact, was so arcane a drug that apparently, but inexplicably, the more inquisitive and talented strata of English society did not know of it. But by the time of Culpeper it was at least known to have some virtues; it was useful, he wrote, in purging, in treating

[1] "Lament for Lleucu Llwyd" in *Medieval Welsh Lyrics,* trans. by Joseph P. Clancy (New York, St. Martin's Press, 1965). Other translators, it appears, rely on the familiar comparison and make "foxglove" a "rose."

sores, "the king's-evil, the falling sickness" and "an ointment thereof is one of the best remedies for a scabby head."

So while science fumbled along, the witches went their usual secret ways and consequently the folk legends, withheld from most townspeople, grew. In addition to the fairy superstitions already noted, there were others more dark: foxgloves, if transplanted, brought disaster upon the owner of their new homeland. This is a curious belief to have arisen, since the plant, being biennial, lives only two years and one would hardly think of transplanting it. We need not worry much, though, for the curse does not go with the seeds, and each plant produces between one and two million seeds. And the names of menace, like dead men's bells, witches' gloves and bloody fingers, may reflect a distant time when the knowing crones prepared foxglove poisons for suspected but unproved crimes of murder.

It may be that the foxgloves were scorned as weeds (except in Wales), for they grow in loamy woodlands and, because of their very small thread-like root systems—small in comparison with the size of the structure of stem, leaves and blossoms—even flourished in crannies of stone walls and rocky areas. Amazing—there it was for all to see, brazenly forcing its attentions on the world with stalks often over four feet high, topped with spikes of drooping, showy, tubular white bells, white, but usually crimson or purplish outside, with dark red spots inside the corolla—and hardly anyone noticed. A biennial, the plant in its first year does not flower, but only produces a rosette of thick leaves from which, in the second year, the flowering stem rises with alternating leaves which diminish in size up to the blooming raceme at the top. Still, no one attended, even to its flagrant beauty, to say nothing of its medicinal properties—except the witches.

When this situation suddenly changed, only in the late eighteenth century, the plant was hailed around the world as a new wonder drug. It has been said that one of the first links between the newly independent colonies of North America and the British Isles was the exchange of drug plants sent back and forth by botanists. Even in 1760 John Bartram was writing his friend, Peter Collinson, in London, "I hope the yellow digitalis and double blossom celandine is come up. . . . All these is very acceptable." But neither man knew what "digitalis" could mean to mankind. It was only in 1785 that any sound report was issued on the uses of the herb. In the meantime, Dr. Erasmus Darwin, grandfather of the more famous Charles, published, in 1780, his prematurely dead son's dissertation on dropsy and added to it some cases involving foxglove. One of the cases which he had, in fact, witnessed was under treatment by Dr. William Withering, but Darwin neglected to even mention his name.

William Withering began practice in Stafford and there became acquainted with a Miss Helena Cookes, a patient, who, as a painter of flowers, lured him into an interest in something he had formerly loathed—botany. The result was that he learned considerably more about plants, though not as much as a certain "witch" had learned, for, as he wrote it down:

> *In the year 1775, my opinion was asked concerning a family receipt for the cure of dropsy. I was told that it had long been kept a secret by an old woman in Shropshire, who had sometimes made cures after the more regular practitioners had failed. I was informed also that the effects produced were violent vomiting and purging; for the diuretic effects seemed to have been overlooked. This medication was composed of twenty or more different herbs; but it was not very difficult for one conversant in these subjects to perceive that the active herb could be no other than Foxglove.*

In spite of the ups and downs of medical acceptance of foxglove as a useful drug, it did finally triumph, despite its late start. After the application of digitalis had been directed, in herbalist fashion, to tuberculosis with negative results, the herb was eventually established as a treatment for what Dr. Withering had always recommended it—cardiac dropsy. Though his part in the discovery had been ignored by Dr. Darwin, Withering did finally gain recognition for his work. At last, in 1785, he published his account of his experiments with the plant, involving about two hundred cases.

Among these cases, however, he had noted some in which foxglove was used in amateur folk-medicine style. He describes a Yorkshire tradesman he visited who had been dosed with "a large handful of green Foxglove leaves in half a pint of water" by his wife. Something more than two to four leaves are enough to kill a man by stoppage of the heart and resultant asphyxiation. Withering wrote of the wife, "This good woman knew the medicine of her country, but not the dose of it, for her husband narrowly escaped with his life." But his own considered use of the herb produced excellent results, and he is now gratefully remembered for it. As a matter of fact, and appropriately, a plant has been named in his honor—*Witheringia*. It is interesting, too, that Benjamin Franklin was one of his patients in London.

The mysterious—a word I do not use loosely—substances in foxglove are glycosides such as digitoxin, digitalin and digitonin. The first of these is a heart stimulant and for some unknown reason, digitonin is a heart depressant. Digitoxin, the stimulant, is the drug used chiefly in cardiac diseases and is now prepared in standardized tablet dosages. Since it is highly poisonous and, being insoluble in water, accumulates in the human system, its medicinal use must be carefully supervised. If digitalis, the combination of the various glycosides which exist in foxglove, is ingested in large amounts it may cause nausea, vomiting, slowing of the pulse, a state in which all objects seem blue, and, possibly, death. The antidote is atropine, but a physician must administer the dosage; in the natural balance of contrarities digitalis is an antidote for poisoning from aconite (monkshood).

This modern knowledge of antidotes is seldom drawn upon in a case of murder. In Paris, in 1863, the young Dr. Pommerais decided to dispose of his mistress, Madame de Pauw, in order to inherit under her will. The means he chose, one which he could easily recommend that the deluded woman herself use, was digitalin. Two honest doctors who were called to treat Mme. de Pauw in her extremity did not recognize symptoms of poisoning and indeed the love-sick lady refused such treatment as they offered. Dr. Pommerais succeeded in disposing of his mistress but his crime was not undetected. Neither did a Brussels widow, Marie Alexandrine Becker in 1938, succeed in avoiding the penalty for murder, again committed with digitalin, though admittedly her harvest considerably overshadowed that of Pommerais—eleven people.[2]

In the fictional world, murder has also been committed by digitalis, but on the level of country folk who know the virtues of herbs, rather than on the level of sophisticated Parisians. In Mary Webb's *Precious Bane,* Gideon Sarn tests foxglove leaves on a cow before he brews it into a tea for his too slowly dying mother:

> *"Come quick, Prue!" she said. "Her's took very bad. The tea didna agree. He says, give it her strong, he says, for it'll do more good the like of that'n. So I did. And she said it was a bitter brew. But she drank it. And in a while she went ever so quiet, and I couldna hear her breathe. And then she gave a guggle and whispers—*

[2] For both cases: Thorwald, *The Century of the Detective,* pp. 308–316.

*" 'Go for Prue.' "*

*I was only just in time to kiss Mother, who was all shrunken down in her pillows. She whispered—*

*"A bitter brew!" and smiled, and caught her breath, and was gone. . . .*

*I sent for the doctor, to see what Mother died of. And he said, were we in the habit of giving her* digitalis, *a strange word I didna know, but he spelled it out for me, and I wrote it down. So I said no, I'd never heard tell of it. So he says, "Foxglove! Foxglove!"*

After the attention focused on foxglove as a valuable medicinal herb by Dr. Withering, those sections of the world which did not have the herb wished to import it. Dr. Withering himself sent seeds to Dr. Hall Jackson of Portsmouth, New Hampshire, who shared them with Dr. Ezra Stiles of Yale College in 1787. In later years the plant has been grown as a commercial drug crop, as well as an ornamental in gardens, because in that way the quality and potency of the drug could be better regulated. Since it produces a million seeds per plant, one would expect the foxglove not merely to "escape cultivation" but to scorn it, and that it has done. It grows wild in various areas over the United States but most thickly in the Pacific Northwest.

What digitalis can do for an ailing heart is astounding; how it accomplishes its results is imperfectly understood. It causes ten quite separate but complicated actions in the body, most of them related to the functioning of the heart, and so, properly administered, is the best cardiac remedy known today. In some strange way it acts as a "governor" to that pumping machine, the heart, tones up its muscle tissues, increases its power of contraction, and, with its additional effect on the arterioles, strengthens and regulates the circulation. Because the drug is also a diuretic and produces a marked effect on the kidneys, it is valuable in treating cardiac edema (as distinct from dropsy related to kidney disorders).

In recent years digitalis is proving valuable as well in combating diseases unrelated to the heart, for which it has been the most important therapeutic agent in the past. At present it has been found beneficial in the treatment of glaucoma and muscular dystrophy and one would be mad to guess what further uses might be discovered for the long-neglected foxglove. If the herbal medicines of "witches' brews" and folk usage need support, they could find no better vindication than in this extraordinary plant.

# Ginkgo Tree

## Ginkgo biloba

*I* hope I am not maligning the beautiful ginkgo tree by including it here. It is just that I may never have another opportunity to pay it, in spite of its mildly objectionable properties, my tribute and respect. I remember a large tree which grew where I lived in the South to which I made many "pilgrimages" each autumn because it turned into a sculptured fountain of pale-gold, lacy leaves, which eventually dropped to spread a yellow sheet across the ground. The tree is gone now, cut down with its owner's house, to make room for a wretched office building of multi-colored baked enamel panels which does not possess one millionth part of the beauty and timelessness of the ginkgo tree.

For this plant has lived on the earth, virtually unchanging, for millions of years, probably longer in its original state than any other existing tree. Its leaves have been found fossilized in rock deposits in the British Isles and the northern Pacific coast of the United States dating from the Jurassic and Triassic periods. It has, in fact, been called a "living fossil." Knowing this, one must think, while looking at this graceful tree today, of all the primordial forms of animal and vegetable life—dinosaurs, pterodac-

*Ginkgo biloba*

tyls, brontosaurs for instance—which once ate its boughs or bowled it over in a mammoth stride, but have now vanished from the earth. Yet the ginkgo tree alone, of all its family, has survived into our time.

In its original home, China, it was a sacred plant and the Chinese planted the trees near their temples. Perhaps even centuries ago, the Chinese knew or sensed how venerable the ginkgo was, just as they knew how to evolve a delicate etiquette which we have never absorbed and now will never be able to practice as even the modern Chinese themselves can not. Those earliest specimens which had grown on the North American continent and in England were apparently wiped out—perhaps by the Ice Age—for the gingkos which grow here now have been imported from Asia and are popular, at present, as trees for parks and fume-choked city streets.

As I have suggested, the gingko is a deciduous tree whose fan-shaped, crinkle-edged leaves, like those of maidenhair fern, drop in the autumn. It is, in fact, often called the maidenhair tree. It sometimes grows as high as one hundred twenty feet, with its branches or shoots sprouting from the main trunk. These divide each year and almost always grow upward, not often outward except in very old trees. Along the shoots short twigs appear and bear the small bunches of spirally arranged leaves.

Except for the prehistoric ferns, the ginkgo's closest relatives are the cycads, palm-like plants with an un-branched columnar trunk and a crown of feathery leaves. Like them it is dioecious, with the male reproductive structure in "flowers" separate from the females, and both sexes springing from the leaf clusters. The male organism is a small pollen cone, indicating the gingko's distant relationship with the conifers. The female "flower," however, is a pair of ovules on a short stem, but in most cases only one of the pair develops fully, while the other withers and becomes a vestigial nub at the base of the cherry-sized fruit.

Though cycads contain an alkaloid, it can be washed out and the starchy stems can be converted into food; in fact, the seeds of bread-palm are used in South Africa to make bread. But the gingko seems to contain no violent poisons and the kernel of the drupes is said to be edible. The pulp around it, however, can cause serious dermatitis when touched. In the autumn, the gingko's fruits fall from the branches while they are still immature and after a few days begin to raise an unpleasant odor as they decompose. Because the seeds are not yet mature, it requires long months for them to germinate after they are planted.

The trees are hardy in reasonably temperate climates and their beauty has brought them into favor with city planners. They are planted more and more along urban streets and in parks. And, if you look carefully, you will find some magnificent specimens in this country.

# Golden Chain Tree

## *Laburnum anagyroides*

$O$ne can only wonder how such a spectacular and poisonous tree could have almost entirely escaped the notice of the ancient sorcerers, physicians, witches and herbalists. It figures rarely in early literature, medicine or history. Theophrastus described it as a bushy tree, like ebony, with similar wood, dense and hard, but made no remarks on its toxic properties. It was grown in Gerard's garden shortly after its introduction into England in the late sixteenth century.

But Culpeper does not mention it. Nor do Muenscher or Kingsbury in their studies of poisonous plants. However, their work is directed primarily to veterinarians and describes plants which may poison grazing stock, and they may have considered it too rare in this country to include in their study. It is nonetheless offered in nurserymen's catalogues and in this rare instance, the dealers warn that it is poisonous and recommend that if you have young children who might put any part of the plant into their mouths, you should "choose another ornamental."

The laburnum is a member of the pulse or bean (legume) family and thus has such cousins as the black locust, precatory bean, locoweeds, lupines, vetch and, of

*Laburnum vulgare*

course, the edible beans and peas. It is indigenous to the mountainous regions of France, Switzerland and southern Germany, but because of the beauty of its flowers it is now cultivated in all parts of the world. In height it reaches to twenty feet and it has smooth, rich brown bark and clover-like leaves. The flowers, which are deep yellow and formed like pea blossoms, hang in racemes as long as a foot and a half—golden chains—which open in the spring and, like all legumes, develop into pods. It is hardy through most of the southeastern part of this country.

Because of the popularity of the tree, various hybrids have been developed to produce purple or other colored flowers and occasionally one of these will produce blooms of three different colors on one tree—purple, red and yellow. Whether hybrid or natural in species, laburnum trees, we are warned, should not be planted where they might overhang a pasture for cows or horses, as the animals might eat the leaves and pods and die.

The poison in laburnum is an alkaloid called cytisine, isolated from the seeds in 1863. It is present in some other species of the family and it causes vomiting, convulsions, frothing at the mouth, a helpless sleepiness and, finally, coma.

# Larkspur

## Delphinium species

*T*he spur, yes—it clearly distinguishes the plant from monkshood. But the lark—where did that come from? Does this flower really suggest the spur of a lark more than of a robin or a nightingale? Gerard also called it larks heel and larks claw. No matter, it has had the name larkspur a long time. Its family name is equally elusive visually. It is from the Greek for dolphin. However, Gerard could see it, and perhaps we can too: "the floures, especially before they be perfected, have a certain shew and likenesse of those Dolphins, which old pictures and armes of certain antient families have expressed with a crooked and bending figure or shape, by which signe also the heavenly Dolphine is set forth."

All that, at least, will give you some idea what the usually blue blossom looks like if you don't already know. What is called larkspur these days is the annual species, sown each spring from seeds; the perennial is usually called by the generic name of delphinium. Larkspur grows moderately high—up to four feet in the best soil and situation—and is in general blue-flowered, though developed varieties produce purple, salmon, rose, and white blossoms. The perennial type, delphinium, does not like

*Delphinium*

hot summer weather and simply gives up if it is forced to try life in such a climate; if gardeners in the torrid zones wish to have the plant, they have to treat it as an annual and plant new rootstock each year. Its usual, natural color, like larkspur, is blue but there are many hybrids with colors ranging to all shades of pale blue and purple, as well as pink, and it can grow to six feet in height. Some of the new varieties are so unnatural they look like plastic fabrications—but every flower degenerator to his own taste.

In contrast to the ecstatic prose of catalogues announcing another new hybrid, consider how simply William Bartram described an unknown natural species in 1777: "Here grows also in abundance a beautiful species of Delphinium; the flowers differ in no respect from those of the common branching Larkspur of the gardens; they are of a fine deep blue color, and disposed in long sparse spikes; the leaves are compound, almost linear, but the segments not so fine cut as those of the garden Larkspur."

Members of the *Delphinium* tribe have the sort of divided, deeply lobed or cleft palmate leaves, which are graceful, fern-like ornaments to so many other plants, poisonous or benign, relative or outsider—monkshood, bleeding heart, anemones, buttercups, hemlock, parsley, and carrot. Other individual characteristics of the plant leaves such as size, intensity of color, presence of hairs, arrangement on the stalk and so forth, help to distinguish among them.

Though the larkspurs are native in Asia Minor, Europe and the United States, most of our native species grow west of the Mississippi River and contain a respectable quota of different alkaloids—four in all but not always in the same species. They were little used in early times as medicine or poison, except for one specific and still valid purpose. Theophrastus gives a few questionable recipes and Pliny described its most lastingly popular medicinal use, as a parasiticide. In the thirteenth century Petrus Crescentius produced his important work on gardening, *Opus Ruralium Commodorum*, and therein, backed up by Pliny, wrote: "The seed made into a powder and mixed with vinegar is a good salve for lice and scabs. That is why it is called lousewort." And lousewort continues to be a name for this particular species, *D. staphisagria*, in England, though a less objectionable name is a corruption of the Latin into "stavesacre."

Of the small larkspur Gerard nevertheless declared, "We finde little extant of the vertues of Larks heele, either in the antient or later writers, worth the noting, or to be credited." Yet the efficacy of the delphinium's juices in destroying body vermin is still notable. It was probably in my college days that I first heard of "Larkspur Lotion," when, on first leaving home for associations with many unknown students, one needed to learn such practical things along with Virgil and Shakespeare. The acrid odor was unmistakable at times in the shower rooms, after some unfortunate host of body lice had used the lotion. I'm sure the medicine worked and is still being sold today, though perhaps not under such a naively candid label.

While the active toxin used in such vermifuges is made from the seeds which are the most potent reservoir of the poison, the other parts of the plant are also dangerous. The level of toxicity in the plant is variable— perhaps lower in cultivated varieties and in the tall larkspurs we call dephiniums, and gradually diminishing in the foliage as the plant lives from season to season. Its wild species, however, rank with locoweed in taking the highest death toll of cattle on pasture lands. The toxic variability extends to the point of affecting cows more readily than horses or sheep. The latter two are only rarely poisoned.

But who are we to challenge the partial immunity of such large animals, when we recall the multiplicity of the alkaloids—delphinine, delphisine, delphinoidine and staphisagroine? The plants which secrete them have been recommended for a few human sicknesses by herb doctors, but not by official medicine, which seems to know no use for them except killing body lice. What a wretched employment for such a charming plant!

# *Lilies*

## *Liliaceae*

*T*he most important dangerous members of this family
have been treated separately—lily of the valley, star-of-
Bethlehem and autumn crocus (meadow saffron). But
there are various other toxic relatives which ought to be
mentioned, at least briefly, because they are favorite garden plants or wild plants delightful enough to be introduced into a garden. Their poisons are varied to some
extent and have various names; many of the poisons are
cardioactive, but in some of the plants little investigation
has been made and little is known about them. Precaution
must remain the watchword, even though many of the
bulbs are cooked as food in some lands, or, less frequently,
eaten raw, just as we eat the lilies called onion, garlic,
shallot, leek, chive and asparagus when they are cultivated. The wild varieties of these vegetables, however, are
not palatable to all people, since they are often on the
rank end of the taste register, but they can be used, especially for seasoning, by an experienced country cook.

There are other edible wild lilies which may be used
as salad or potherbs: corn-lily or cow-tongue (*Clintonia
borealis*); wake-robin (*Trillium*); several varieties of
*Smilax*; and the young shoots of both the true and the

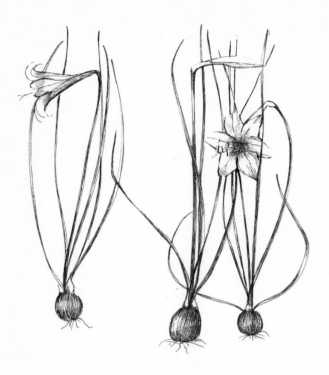

*Zephyranthes atamasco*

false Solomon's seal. These plants and some of the other wild lilies not cited are becoming so rare in our vanishing woodlands that their consumption is to be discouraged. A not at all scarce wild lily, with better flavor and more uses, is the familiar yellow day lily or lemon lily (*Hemerocallis fulva* or *flava*). It grows fast, spreads fast and indeed has been recommended as a garden vegetable, as it is used in China and Japan in the form of dried flowers (then called *gum-jum* or *gum-tsoy*). The roots of day lilies can be boiled in salted water and eaten, or if they are young, even tried raw in a salad. In spring the new shoots can be a vegetable; later, the full unopened buds can be boiled, fried in a batter or added to soup.[1] Just be sure you have the right lily, for others are not so benign.

It is not surprising that the lily, which produces such a showy, even spectacular flower, became sacred to gods and kings and, especially when pure white, a symbol of purity and virtue. In the ancient civilizations of Sumer, Babylon and Egypt it signified fertility. It was the royal emblem of the king of Knossos, who appears surrounded by lilies on a relief in the surviving palace ruins. It was the insignia of Grecian Hera and Roman Juno, goddesses of women, marriage and motherhood. It seems only natural then that the lily should be associated with the Virgin Mary and should recur over and over again in paintings of her done in the Renaissance. And that it should become the symbol of Easter.

What we call the Madonna lily is the *Lilium candidum*, of which the Greeks and Romans most often wrote. Theophrastus, who confused many plants and notions, has little to offer us for our brief summary, but Pliny, while confusing the morning glory blossom with the lily blossom, and repeating Theophrastus' error in saying that the lily reproduces by an "exudation"—"a peculiar tear-like gum of its own"—had apparently read of or observed lilies more carefully. At any rate, he gives us the medicinal uses of the plant in his day. "Its roots," he says, "bring great fame to the lily in many ways, being taken in wine for the bites of snakes and for poisoning by fungi. For corns on the foot they are boiled down in wine, and the

[1] On several lilies: Merritt Lyndon Fernald and Alfred Charles Kinsey, *Edible Wild Plants of Eastern North America*, revised by Reed C. Rollins (New York, Harper and Brothers Publishers, 1958) pp. 126–143.

[2] On day lilies: Euell Gibbons, *Stalking the Wild Asparagus* (New York, David McKay Company Inc., 1962), pp. 83–86.

plaster is not removed for three days. Boiled down with grease or oil they also make hair grow again on burns." More serious uses, which are less exactly explained, are indicated for treatment of the spleen, swollen testicles, ruptures, spasms, menstrual discharge, deep cuts, leprous sores, scurf, wrinkles, erysipelas and boils. All this is repeated in one way or another by Dioscorides, Crescentius and later herbalists. If one can pierce through his seventeenth century English, Culpeper can always give you a turn, or a chuckle: the crushed flowers and roots are good "to break imposthumations" and an ointment of them is "good for swellings in the privities" or to "trimly deck a blank space with hair." Gerard, who on the whole is less taken in by the ancients, tells us that the stamped bulb "gleweth together sinues that be cut in sunder." But he makes a comment on what poets have written:

> . . . *that* Hercules, *who* Jupiter *had by* Alcumena, *was put to* Juno's *breasts whilest she was asleepe; and after the sucking there fell away abundance of milk, and that one part was spilt in the heavens, and the other upon the earth; and that of this sprang the Lilly, and of the other the circle in the heavens called* Lacteus Circulus, *or the Milky way, or otherwise in English Watling Street.*

Aside from the *Lilium candidum* which we call Madonna lily or Easter lily (though the latter name is usually given to *L. longiflorum eximium,* and there are minor but distinct differences between the two plants), the popular lilies in this country are the climbing *Gloriosa* lily, the spider lily, the tiger lily, the Turk's-cap and martagon lilies. These last two names are often used synonymously, particularly in England, but some slight distinctions should be made because of American usage.

Martagon, being a generic name, could describe the group which includes the long-familiar dark purple, black-spotted cottage lily of England called martagon; the native American (eastern United States) Turk's-cap (*L. superbum*), over seven feet high, orange and yellow with purple spots; the leopard or panther lily (*L. pardalinum*), a tall orange-red and yellow, speckled native of the western mountains; or the oriental introduction, now often growing wild in the United States, the tiger lily (*L. tigrinum*), over six feet high with spotted orange flowers and, as an identification tag, a habit of producing small black bulblets in the axils of the leaves. Turk's-cap could describe these lilies just as well, with their strongly reflexed petals, but some resemble a turban, a neatly rolled one, more aptly than others.

The vine-like glory lily contains a poison very similar to colchicine (from autumn crocus) and is patently dangerous. Even the pollen from tiger lilies—lilies are notorious for the great amount of pollen they produce and scatter from their anthers at any disturbance—has poisoned some people, causing drowsiness, purging and vomiting. In the Renaissance period the bulbs of white lilies, compounded with honey, wax and rosewater, produced a pomatum to remove wrinkles—an early form of cold cream. A drug, useful, it is said, in treating uterine disturbances, is extracted from the white lily. As to the martagon, Gerard offered a philosophical approach: "There hath not bin any thing left in writing either of the nature of vertues of these plants: notwithstanding we may deem, that God which gave them such seemely and beautifull shape, hath not left them without their peculiar vertues, the finding out whereof we leave to the learned and industrious searcher of Nature." That searcher must already have existed but must not have been learned enough to leave his findings in writing; for martagon must contain some dire juices, since it is one of the several deadly plants collected by Ben Jonson's witch.

In early writings it is difficult to discern exactly

which plant, according to our present names, is being talked about. What we call hyacinth is not so called in Theophrastus or Pliny: the latter, describing *hyacinthus*, is really talking about gladiolus or scilla; the former mentions *hyakinthos* but defined it as the "wild kind" (squill) and the "cultivated" (larkspur). Here indeed is a shock— two most dissimilar plants lumped together as hyacinths. Robert Graves states that the hyacinth in Homer was a blue larkspur, which was also sacred to the Cretan flower-hero, Hyacinthus, who was also called Narcissus. Let us not plunge deeper into this tangle of identities!

Up to the sixteenth century our modern hyacinth (but certainly not in its highly developed hybrid forms) was often being treated as a lily which, of course, it is. Gerard lists the wild jacinth, or hare-bells, of England— white, blue or pink—and under "red lilies" discusses the "Poet's Hyacinth," the one which should have imprinted on its petals Apollo's cry of woe, "Ai," uttered at the death of the beloved youth from whose blood the flower sprang. As Ovid told it:

> *The blood that filled the grasses at his feet*
> *Turned to a brighter dye than Tyrian purple,*
> *And from its lips there came a lily flower,*
> *And yet, unlike the silver-white of lilies,*
> *Its colour was a tinted, pinkish blue.*
> *Nor was this miracle enough for Phoebus;*
> *He wrote the words "Ai, Ai" across its petals,*
> *The sign of his own grief, his signature.*[3]

But neither lilies nor hyacinths as we know them have any markings on the petals which could be said to resemble "Ai." What *was* this plant? We already have noted the possibility of its being squill or larkspur and, among other guesses, the wild blue flag, the iris, the gladiolus have been offered.

[3] Ovid, *The Metamorphoses*, trans. by Horace Gregory (New York, The Viking Press, 1958).

At any rate, our contemporary hyacinth is poisonous whether it was two, three or four thousand years ago or not. During the Middle Ages its roots were one of the ingredients of an ointment intended to cure leprosy sores. Though Culpeper briefly describes eight kinds of hyacinth as the most beautiful, he can find little—good or bad—to say about them: "The root is full of a slimy juice, a decoction of which operates by urine. . . . Its virtues are little known, it will cure the whites, the fresh root is poisonous, and may be made into starch."

Our densely flowered garden varieties originated in oriental species, but many charming, graceful and less obtrusive native kinds are available. Grape hyacinth, with its compact spikes of deep blue or white bells, so closed as to resemble grapes on a stem, grows less than a foot high and has a heavy sweet odor—musky, as its genus, *Muscari*, indicates. This plant was recommended by Pseudo-Apuleius for treatment of gout and dropsy and, in a poultice of crushed bulbs, for boils. These bulbs are poisonous and have a stimulant and diuretic effect; comisic acid has been extracted from them.

Squills (*Scilla species*) are often mistaken for wild hyacinths and with good reason in view of their appearance, but they are different in important ways. For instance, unlike hyacinths, they have a history of medicinal usage dating back about four thousand years to the Egyptian Ebers Papyrus, which gives as a remedy for heart troubles a recipe including the bulbs of squills. Hippocrates recommended them for dropsy, and he was no more wrong, within some limits, than the Egyptians. Theophrastus and Dioscorides had much to say of squills and Pliny synthesizes their information in his own work. Squill vinegar, he held, was beneficial for dull vision, abdominal pains, tapeworm, "epilepsy, melancolia, giddiness, hysterical suffocations . . . and affections of the kidneys"; but he warned, "so great is its strength that too copious a draught produces for a moment the appearance of death." Otherwise prepared, the bulbs were used for dropsy, jaundice, indigestion and asthmatic coughs. The leaves, too, would clear up scrofula "if they are left on for four days"—a rather messy treatment!

From their day to the present, squill has been used in the preparation of medicines and it is also an ornamental in our gardens. However—the tangled skeins of identification rise once more—the plant referred to medicinally by those ancients as squill has now been removed from the genus *Scilla*; it once was classified as *S. maritima* and called sea onion because its huge bulb grows half-buried in the sand on the seacoast of the Mediterranean and in other dry places, where it rears stems of flowers up to three feet high—hardly like our demure garden scilla. In 1834, after thorough examination, the therapeutic squill was given the name *Urginea*, to commemorate the home of the Algerian tribe where investigations of it had taken place. The bulb from which various cardioactive, diuretic and emetic glycosides have been isolated—scillitoxin, scillipicrin, scillin, for example—can grow large enough to weigh four pounds. Over the years numerous pills, extracts, syrups and other fluid medicines have been compounded with squill as the active ingredient. Though these are still in use, their application to heart disease, like that of convallatoxin (from lily of the valley), was appreciably reduced after the discovery of digitalis, but their proven value remains unchallenged.

Our garden squills, though closely related to this giant bulbous *Urginea*, hardly grow more than a foot tall. But they contain, in a lesser degree, similar poisons and have been used as substitutes for the official *Urginea*. The very name, *Scilla*, comes from a Greek word meaning "disturbing," as an emetic disturbs the stomach. That is one symptom of poisoning from squills; others are severe inflammation of the digestive and urinary tracts, convulsions, poor circulation and, possibly, death. Death would almost surely result from eating a product of the squill *Urginea*, which is known as red squill powder and is manufactured as a rodent poison.

The tulip (*Tulipa species*), one of the favorite spring flowers, has no such long history of therapeutic use. We associate it, as well as hyacinths, with Holland, where it has been bred and developed for years. It is a Persian plant, called *lálé*, and was imported in the sixteenth century, apparently by the Flemish ambassador to Constantinople. The tulip symbolizes the perfect lover to the Persians, and in their legend the flower originated in the tears shed by a rejected lover as he wept himself to death in the desert.

By some, tulips are assumed to have been the Biblical "lilies of the field." The name itself is derived from Turkish *tulipant*, meaning "turban," and so it was called Turk's-cap; Gerard also called it Dalmatian cap but said that nothing was known of its virtues. Agreeing with other writers, he noted that the roots, if preserved in sugar, were good. Parkinson announced that the roots were nourishing, "for divers have had them sent by their friends from beyond the seas and mistaking them to be onions have used them as such in their pottage or broth." The accumulating evidence would not support these claims today, unless cooking nullifies whatever noxious juice is in them, for people have been poisoned by eating the bulbs. Dioscorides suggested that the seeds were valuable as an aphrodisiac. The only medicinal prescription for the tulip which I have been able to find was given, oddly enough, by a poet. Abraham Cowley wrote of it:

> *I am a flow'r for sight, a drug for use,*
> *By secret virtue and resistless power*
> *Those whom the jaundice seizes I restore;*
> *The dropsie headlong makes away*
> *As soon as I my arms display.*

Did an old herb woman tell him a secret no one else knew?

The same lack of knowledge about the "vertues" of the tulip holds for fritillary. *Fritillaria meleagris*, one of the popular species, is known by a variety of common names—checkered daffodil or lily, and guinea hen flower both describe the drooping tulip-shaped blossom and roughly translate the two botanical names. For the flower is amazingly marked off in two-colored spots which are almost squares. Two other fritillaries mentioned by Gerard with this one—Persian lily (*F. persica*) and crown imperial (*F. Imperialis*)—were introduced into England from Persia in 1596 and the crown imperial is unusual in a different way from the checkered daffodil. Its flowers emerge all around the top of a three-foot stalk, and hang down, bell-like, yellow, orange or red, while above them rises a thick tuft of upright leaves. Even more unusual is that each flower holds at the bottom of its bell, as Gerard put it, "sixe drops of most cleare shining sweet water, in taste like sugar, resembling in shew faire orient pearles; the which drops if you take away, there do immediately appeare the like." It must have been this plant of which Shelley wrote:

> *That tall flower that wets—*
> *Like a child, half in tenderness and mirth—*
> *His mother's face with Heaven-collected years*
> *When the low wind, its playmate's voice it hears.*

The bulbs of this species were cooked and eaten by the Persians and valued as medicine by the Chinese. But eaten raw they are poisonous, affecting the heart, just like the bulbs of checkered daffodil, which are much smaller, hardly even bite-sized. Grieve and Leyel report that an alkaloid, imperialine, was isolated from crown imperial in 1888, but little is known of the toxic nature of the fritillaries.

The checkered, guinea hen species grows wild in

England, and in the United States there are many native wild varieties which I should think anyone would want in a garden, if they could survive. One called mission bells (*F. lanceolata*) is notable for the delicacy of its separated slender petals with the "clapper" of reproductive elements inside—really more like some oriental bell than one from a mission. Another unusual quality is that it appears to be non-poisonous, for the Indians and early white settlers used to eat its roots, raw or boiled. All other fritillaries are either known to be poisonous or are under dark suspicion.

There are many other wild native genera of the lily family which might be introduced into a garden—more and more the wild varieties are being captured by nurserymen and offered for sale. A common one, if the garden is spacious, and a surprising one to find in the lily family, is Spanish bayonet (*Yucca torreyi*) and its relatives. It is highly improbable, of course, that anyone will brave those low spiney daggers to get a chance to gnaw on the plant. Scientists today are pursuing the presence in yucca, as well as in the similar but fleshier *Agave,* of saponin compounds, which destroy red blood cells.

Two wild members of the lilies which might appeal to the gardener are the tall, showy Osceola's plume of the southeast and, less probably, a wild hyacinth. The first, like all members of its genus, *Zygadenus*, is extremely poisonous. The second may be a type of "wild" hyacinth with an edible bulb, which the Indians called "quamash," from which it took the generic name *Camassia*, with *scilloides* to indicate a resemblance to squills. Today these are listed in flower catalogues. But you may think the squill-like plant called camass is the one for you, if you are searching for them in the woods. Alas, this one is another *Zygadenus*, and for very good reasons carries an adjective with its name—death camass.

# *Lily of the Valley*

## *Convallaria majalis*

"*I* am the Rose of Sharon, and the lily of the valley," exults the Song of Solomon. By some investigators, the Rose of Sharon is thought not to have been the plant we call by that name, the althea (*Hibiscus*), but the tulip. Was the lily of the valley something different to the dwellers in ancient Asia Minor? Or has its identity persisted along with its name, probably through the Vulgate Bible, to the herbalists? Gerard says, "The Latines have called it Lilium Convallium" (rather literally translated by our current name) and adds that it is called "in some places Liriconfancie"—obviously by people who distorted the Latin in their attempts to pronounce it. When in the eighteenth century, Carolus Linnaeus established his system of botanical classification, he retained the roots of the description in *Convallaria*.

It is native in Europe and the Levant and in the Allegheny mountains of this country. Wild though it is, it is beloved of many people for the sleek, bright, canoe-like leaves, the delicate sprays of white (or, in some cases, pale pink) bell-flowers, and the delicious odor. It is too ingratiating, really; it will happily grow wild in shaded woodlands and carpet a broad area, or it will thrive in a

*Convallaria majalis*

garden border, or flourish and bloom in a pot to bring premature spring to a wintry room.

It belongs to the large lily family, so many of whose members have a bad habit of producing toxins in their bodies, but it does not, as most lilies do, spring from a large bulb. One plants "pips," sections of the thick main root, which spread vigorously in rich porous soil and thus carpet a surrounding area. The flower stalk shoots up between the two or three leaves to a height of eight or ten inches, with the blossoms hanging like bells of six fused "petals." If the flowers mature into seed, which is not often, they will appear as red berries, similar to those on asparagus.

The plant was known to contain a drug at least from the time of the fifteenth century when the *Hortus Sanitatis,* "Garden of Health," published a recipe using the flowers, which would prevent apoplexy for a month; furthermore, if the potion were rubbed on the forehead and the back of the neck it would make a person "to have good common sense." Perhaps we need to use this recipe widely in our contemporary world.

Gerard also reports that it is good for apoplexy and gout, but comes closest to truth as we know it in saying that it can "comfort the heart." For the poison that hides in this lovely plant is very similar to digitalis. Or should I rephrase my subject as plural—poisons—since it has been stated that the lily of the valley is rich with *two* glycosides, convallarin and convallamarin? Just how we may distinguish between them need not concern us here. We may take the testimony of French analysts who have reported that four drops of the poison extracted from the plant, injected into the veins of a dog, could kill it in ten minutes. Still, that poison is a cardioactive drug and even today the extract from the roots and rhizome of the plant is important, second only to digitalis, in the treatment of heart diseases.

The taste of lily of the valley is apparently bitter or, at least, unpleasant, and few animals eat the wild plants. But, as ever, in view of the curiosity and undiscriminating tastes of children, with the plant in reach in gardens and inside the house, it is well to be careful and to instruct the children about its dangers. Unmindful of that bitter taste, a five-year-old girl, being thirsty and untended, or for some strange reason, drank the water from a glass in which a bunch of lily of the valley had been standing. As we know, a viscous juice oozes from the plant when cut and the seepage of this into the water took the girl's life.

# Monkshood

## Aconitum napellus

*T*here it is, bright, beautiful and inviting, in the catalogue's color photo, ready to be ordered in clumps of roots
and set in your garden. A handsome plant, growing up to
three feet high, with dark green glistening leaves, palmate
and deeply cut like the leaves of its relative, larkspur, and
with blue flowers (though in some species they are white
or yellow) clustered at the top of the stems, it has long
been cultivated as an ornamental in gardens. It has also
long been cultivated as a drug plant whose poison, though
concentrated most powerfully in the tuberous roots, extends to every part of the plant and has been called "one of
the most formidable poisons which have yet been discovered."

Its family name, with no possible relevance to one of
Gilbert and Sullivan's characters, is buttercup (or crowfoot). We hear of it from the most ancient of recorded
times, for its habitat stretches from Japan, China and the
Himalayas westward across Asia Minor and Europe, and,
in the native American species, across this continent. Its
botanical name, like much of its legend, is from Greece—
Theophrastus explains, "It grows everywhere and not only
at Akonai, from whence it gets its name"; and its early

*(90)*

*Aconitum napellus*

English common name, wolfsbane, is a translation of one of the secondary names Theophrastus gave it while relating that it was also called "scorpion-plant" because it "kills that animal if it is shredded over him."

The legends of aconite reach much farther back in time. We don't know for certain that this poison was used forty-five hundred years before Christ by Gula, the Sumerian goddess of disease, health and sorcery, but why should she not have had it? Interestingly, her symbol was a dog, and her Greek counterpart in witchcraft, Hecate, had a retinue of dogs. And it was from a very special dog, through that favorite Attic explanation of origins, metamorphosis, that aconite came. The twelfth labor of Hercules required him to bring up to earth the watchdog of the portals of Hades. This dog, Cerberus, had anywhere from three to fifty heads (which version of the myth are you reading?) and—choose one—a tail of venom-dribbling serpents or a collar of serpents around each neck. I need not tell you that Hercules succeeded in dragging this child of the giant Typhoeus and Echidna from the underworld, but few of us who have lovely monkshood nodding in our gardens are aware that it sprang from the frothing poison which dropped on the hills of Pontica from the raging animal's mouths before Hercules could take him back below. Some say his spittle poisoned already-growing herbs, some that Hecate used his vomit to concoct a toxic brew. The truth is evident, on any legendary level: aconite was generated by the furious froth of Cerberus.

As Hecate's disciple, Medea used it in her attempt to kill Theseus. As Ovid puts it, in A. E. Watts' translation:

> *For him Medea mixed, with murderous thought,*
> *A draught of aconite, from Scythia brought,*
> *From Cerber's teeth the plant was grown, they say.*

From Cerberus' teeth? Well, they are *somewhat* like seeds; but then Ovid was centuries after the fact, and legends tend to degenerate in the retelling.

But no serious legend ever attempted to discount the deadly potential of monkshood. Devoted herbalists and homeopaths of old have endeavored to find useful purposes for the vicious but pretty plant, following Theophrastus, possibly, in his prescription of how to kill a scorpion, to rather frivolous ends. He had propounded a schedule for regulating the time of death by the time when the roots were gathered, for he thought the poison worked very slowly. Gerard, usually of an inquiring mind, announced that an antidote to the bite of the "Tarantala" was a concoction of flies which had fed on the plant. The antidote for poisoned human beings, as described by Avicenna, was a mouse nourished on aconite, though others say that the prescription may be an error of a copyist of his manuscript. At any rate, we get a glimmer in this of the fumblings of early scientists toward the theories behind our modern knowledge of serums and vaccines.

Culpeper and John Parkinson both thought one species with yellow flowers was a "counter-poison monkeshood," and, as the latter put it: "the roots of which are effectual, not only against the poison of the poisonful Helmet Flower [another name for monkshood], and all others of that kind, but also against the poison of all venomous beasts, the plague or pestilence and other infectious diseases, which raise spots, pockes, or markes in the outward skin." Culpeper himself is rather more cautious, for he says, preserving the usual reticence of the homeopath in regard to poisonous plants, "it is not much regarded at this time, and should be cautiously kept out of children's way, for there is a farina in the flower, which is very dangerous if blown in the eyes; the leaves also, if rubbed on the skin, will irritate and cause soreness."

The earlier writers were not quite so restrained as to the lethal attributes of aconite. Nicander, the Greek physician, wrote:

> *You have indeed to learn about the aconite,*
> *Bitter as gall and deadly in the mouth, a blight*
> *The banks of Acheron produced.*

Virgil expressed the Romans' loathing of the plant in his *Second Georgic*:

> *Nor poisonous aconite is here produced,*
> *Or grown unknown, or is, when grown, refused.*

But certainly it continued through all the centuries, from Hecate and Medea, to maintain its place in the witches' pharmacy of magic simples and, along with belladonna, was a prime ingredient in the ointment witches used for "flying." Even applied to the skin, belladonna can produce a degree of delirium, and aconite, by causing an irregular action of the heart, can give a sensation of rising and falling—thus combined, in fact, a feeling of zooming through the air. But that was witches' lore, the secrets and superstitions of a chosen few. The scientist's, the investigator's, lore was not entirely lagging. The deadly effects of monkshood were recognized, as they always had been, but now were better understood and emphasized.

In his *New Herball*, William Turner contradicted Theophrastus on the slow effects of aconite, "This Wolf's bayne of all poison is the most hastie poison." And he proceeded to caution: "Let oure Londiners which of late have receyved this blewe wolfes bayne otherwyse called Monkes coule, take hede that the poyson of the rote of this herbe one daye do not more harme than the freshnes of the flower hath done pleasure in seven yeres; let them not saye but they are warned." I fear not many people heeded.

Considering the confusion existing in plant identification and the scores of herbs which Gerard grew in his garden, it cannot truly astonish us that he should sometimes confuse matters, as he did in calling a true buttercup an aconite. He reported as yellow wolfsbane the plant which poisoned "Mr. *Mahewe* dwelling in Boston, a student in physick," who, "having occasion to ride through the fens of Lincolnshire, found a root that the hogs had turned up, which seemed unto him very strange and unknowne, for that it was in the spring before the leaves were out: this he tasted, and it so inflamed his mouth, tongue, and lips, that it caused them to swell very extremely so that before he could get to the towne of Boston, he could not speake, and no doubt had lost his life if that the Lord God had not blessed those good remedies which presently he procured and used." Gerard's first editor, Thomas Johnson, in revising the herbal later, commented that what Mr. Mahewe ate was in fact *Ranunculus* (buttercup).

On more solid ground, Gerard refers to a case of poisoning by true aconite: "The force and facultie of Wolfs-bane is deadly to man and all kindes of beasts: the same was tried of late in Antwerpe, and is as yet fresh in memorie, by an evident experiment, but most lamentable; for when the leaves hereof were by certain ignorant persons served up in sallads, all that did eat thereof were presently taken with most cruell symptomes, and so died." The symptoms: "their lipps and tongue swell forthwith, their eyes hang out, their thighes are stiffe, and their wits are taken from them."

In view of this, perhaps we should not be too scornful of much later writers who seemed to lean toward an exaggeration amounting to superstition in commenting on the deadly nature of monkshood. Henry Phillips (*Flora Historica*, c. 1829) claimed that people had swooned and lost their sight from "taking the effluvia of the herb by the nostrils." And in his *Rural Rides* William Cobbett warned that the plant is poisonous "even when injudiciously smelled to." Possible, yes. At the same time, does not this modern twentieth century resumé by two scholars[1] of monkshood's virulence seem like exaggeration? "One fiftieth grain of Aconitine [one of the alkaloids extracted from the plant] will kill a sparrow in a few seconds; one-tenth grain a rabbit in five minutes. . . . One hundredth grain will act locally, so as to produce a well-marked sensation in any part of the body for a whole day. So acrid is the poison, that the juice applied to a wounded finger affects the whole system, not only causing pains in the limbs, but a sense of suffocation and syncope."

So virulent an herb could hardly fail to be well known to most people and to be utilized by poets, especially the dramatic poets of Elizabeth's day. One can, in a short essay, choose only a sample. In *Sejanus*, Ben Jonson refers to aconite as a cure for the bite of a scorpion, harking back to Theophrastus, and perhaps, in his witch's song:

> *I've been plucking (plants among)*
> *Hemlock, henbane, adder's tongue,*
> *Nightshade, moonwort, leppardsbane.*

Under the heading of "leopards bane" in his herbal, Gerard had struggled to disentangle earlier descriptions of plants and their names, and gave to leopard's bane many of the attributes of aconite; though he names it, in Latin, *Doronicum pardalianches*, he later, more correctly, calls it aconite.[2] *Doronicum* is a showy, daisy-like, apparently dangerous plant which Gerard's modern editor says is "an

[1] Mrs. M. Grieve and Mrs. C. F. Leyel, *A Modern Herbal*, two volumes (New York, Harcourt Brace and Company, 1931).

[2] Gerard was not alone among the early herbalists in confusing leopard's bane and wolfsbane. The woodcut from Mattioli's *Commentaries on Dioscorides* (1563) labelled aconite, which is reproduced in Joseph Wood Krutch's recent *Herbal*, seems to be *Doronicum pardialanches*, or *D. cordatum*, the "scorpion-plant" of Theophrastus.

outcast from gardens in Britain." Not so in the United States: it is described in a nursery list as "harmful to leopards, but that need not worry many gardeners!" Keats, however, is thinking of the first-known, simple lethal effect of monkshood when he cries out in his "Ode on Melancholy":

> *No, no, go not to Lethe, neither twist*
> *Wolf's-bane, tight-rooted, for its poisonous wine.*

In the Orient, as in the Occident, the native species of aconite were, in ancient times, adapted to poisoning arrow and spear points and to a variety of medicinal purposes. There are small physical differences in the plants from Japan westward around the earth to the Pacific Coast, but the plants are all poisonous, usually deadly. Yet one of the most potent in lethal properties, *A. napellus* (a name referring not to Naples but to the tuberous root, like a turnip), was introduced into England and the United States in the days when its possibilities as a drug made it appear advisable to do so. In June of 1760 John Bartram was writing a friend, thanking him for sending plants and seeds, that "Many aconites is come up," which may have been the *napellus* species, the preferred one for medicine. Later in his letter he adds: "My aconite that I brought from James River last fall, if it be it grows finely and though in its native place sends forth but one stalk from one root, yet mine hath now five stalks and by its forward growth it may flower two month sooner than it did last fall, yet I hope to continue it in flower till frost if I don't let it seed to send to you."

But however it was introduced (for it has escaped from cultivation and is naturalized, though rare, in the northeast), the transatlantic trip of *A. napellus* seems hardly necessary. We already had several of our own indigenous monkshoods, though perhaps not as powerful as *A. napellus*, and they are still with us. Annually they poison scores of grazing stock, and yet field mice, it is reported, even in times of starvation, will not so much as nibble at the plant.

Aside from the poisoning of hunting weapons to kill game, little consistently beneficial application for aconite has been found. One could, of course, rid one's home of rats with it, if the medieval *Le Ménagier de Paris* is right: "Make cakes of paste and toasted cheese and powdered aconite and set these near their holes." It has been recommended, in the minutest dosages, for pleurisy, neuralgia, aneurism and of course, because it is a heart depressant, in cardiac illnesses. Externally, in ointments and liniments, it has recently been used, not to my knowledge for flying on broomsticks, but for such discomforts as rheumatism and lumbago. Presumably it is still official in England and Europe, but the United States omitted aconite from its pharmacy in 1942. Probably its dangerously high potency and its side effects outweighed its value as a drug compared with the new synthetic and plant drugs that were being discovered and developed.

Why, then, is monkshood offered as a garden ornamental in catalogues and cultivated by flower-lovers? First, perhaps, because of ignorance of the killer it harbors, but second, assuredly, because it is a pretty plant with delightful flowers. It can be mistaken for its cousin, larkspur, by those who are not observant of minute details: the height of the two plants is more or less equal, the leaves are very similar and the flowers seem, at a short distance, to be the same. But the brightly colored upper sepal of the larkspur blossom projects backward as a spur; the top sepal of monkshood simply curves up and over to form a hood. And monkshood grows from a tuber, which the larkspur-delphiniums do not do. Another difference is that a few nibbles of monkshood may kill you or your child, while the same snack off a larkspur may merely make you deathly ill.

There are two principal alkaloids in all parts of

aconite, or monkshood—aconitine and aconine—and they seem to be most potent just before the plant flowers. To the description of the symptoms they cause, which has already been quoted from Gerard, I might add nausea, stomach pains, difficult breathing, faint and erratic pulse, staggering, and "a sensation of ants crawling over the body." Since aconite is a cardiac depressant, the obvious antidote is a heart stimulant—that is, another poison, digitalis or atropine. But these drugs must be administered by a physician, lest you poison the patient with the antidote.

Maybe the best course, if you have small children, is just not to have monkshood, lovely, limpid-blue though its flowers may be, in your garden.

# Mountain Laurel and Rhododendron

## Kalmia latifolia and Rhododendron species

*T*his shrub, one of the most beautiful plants native to the United States, was "discovered" in the eighteenth century by a Swedish botanist, Peter Kalm, and the genus bears his name. It grows from New England and the eastern Great Lakes region southward along the Appalachians to northern Florida. Its favorite site is the edge of a wood, where its cousins, the azaleas and rhododendrons, flourish. Small wonder that, arrayed in softly vibrant billows of rose, pink and white in such a conspicuous showplace, they could impress even the most hardened frontiersman. Certainly they have impressed gardeners who are able to provide suitably acid soil (by adding leaf mold), and the proper situation (semi-shade) and climate. The shrubs, which are evergreen and grow as high as ten feet or more, used to be ravaged from the woodlands and transplanted in the garden; small plants can now be obtained, rather expensively, through nurseries.

*Kalmia latifolia*

Like cherry laurel, it is not a true laurel—those smooth, simple oblong leaves have attracted the laurel name to many plants quite different from the genus *Laurus* except in their leaves. The mountain laurel belongs to the heath family. The flowers appear in corymbs, and each one is fascinating in color and form. They change hues almost by the hour, as the bud, rich rose, like a rosette on a birthday cake or, faced head-on, like a fat asterisk, begins to open, to fade to paler pink and almost white, but with ten specks of rose ringing it to reflect the vanished color. Those ten specks of color form the asterisk face of the bud—a puckered sugarplum, a ten-pointed star—for they are pouches in which the ten anthers of the stamens are snared when the bud unfolds, leaving a single pistil standing from the center. The flower is a cup, a calyx of five sepals fused into a single unit. At a touch on the flower, the anthers will spring from their rosy traps with a shower of pollen. In describing her American tour during 1830, Mrs. Trollope referred to the mountain laurel she saw in the Alleghenies as "that beautiful mischief, the *kalmia."*

What a complex, lovely flower! What a pity the plant contains poison! In its leaves, as in those of many other members of the heath family, there is a toxic substance called andromedotoxin, which has caused death in human beings and animals. The fact that one of the smaller species (*K. angustifolia*) has the common names of lambkill and calfkill should, therefore, need no elaboration.

J. W. Harshberger has reported the story of a troupe of trained goats which was performing in a Philadelphia theatre. The stage had been decorated with branches of mountain laurel on which the goats munched between acts—whether out of hunger or stage fright is not indicated—and six members of the troupe died. The managers of zoos have to be careful that mountain laurel and its cousin, rhododendron, though excellent background shrubs, will not be planted within reach of the animal specimens, or within reach of visitors who like to "feed the animals." It ought to be said, however, that animals do not readily take to the tough leathery leaves and it is even less likely that children would chew on them. Still, the adventurous, curious experiments which children will make are always unpredictable.

Rhododendron (Greek for "rose-tree"), along with several other members of the heath family, shares at least one major characteristic with mountain laurel—its poison, andromedotoxin. The other shrubs vary in one or another respect, shape of leaves, flowers, arrangement of blossoms and so on, but rhododendron is very similar to mountain laurel except in its dimensions and flowers. It can reach a height of over fifteen feet and produces long, ovate glossy leaves, but the flowers are more like those of azalea than of mountain laurel. Unlike the fused bell of the *Kalmia* blossom, the rhododendron blossom opens out its five petals as separate units in a terminal corymb, so that, even more spectacularly than *Kalmia*, each branch of rhododendron seems to produce a large nosegay.

It grew in Greece and Asia Minor, as it does in one form or another almost everywhere, but the early commentators on it, not unexpectedly, did not discriminate enough for us always to be able to identify a given plant. The Greeks and Pliny used the names rhododaphne, rhododendron and nerium for a variety of similar plants. One cannot be sure whether they are talking about our rhododendron, our oleander or some other plant. The honey which Xenophon reported as having been poisoned by bees feeding on rhododendron was probably poisoned by their feeding on oleander (*nerium*).

Again, hear Mrs. Trollope in the Alleghenies where she seemed to respond with more delight to the natural setting than to the "domestic manners" of the Americans: ". . . the magnificent *rhododendron* first caught our eyes; it fringes every cliff, nestles beneath every rock, and blooms around every tree." More exciting to me, however, is the record of William Bartram's discovery of a new species fifty years ahead of Mrs. Trollope's discovery of America:

> *This species of Rhododendron grows six or seven feet high; many nearly erect stems arise together from the root, forming a group or coppice. The leaves are three or four inches in length, of an*

> *oblong figure, broadest toward the extremity, and terminating with an obtuse point; their upper surface of a deep green and polished; but the nether surface of a rusty iron colour, which seems to be effected by innumerable minute red vesicles, beneath a fine short downy pubescence; the numerous flexile branches terminate with a loose spiked raceme, or cluster of large deep rose coloured flowers, each flower being affixed in the diffused cluster of a long peduncle, which, with the whole plant, possesses an agreeable perfume.*

This was *R. ferrugineum*, one of the more than twenty native American species. But this evergreen shrub grows around the globe, in Europe and Asia. There is even one which grows in low dense mats with tiny leaves, ranging from the Arctic down through Canada and into the northeastern United States, from which a not very palatable tea can be made; it is called Lapland rosebay (*R. lapponicum*). The most usual colors for rhododendron flowers are in the range from white to rose or red, though there are some species with yellow blossoms.

Needless to say, given such a beautiful plant, the hybridizers were not long idle. Today there are many variations available in colors which shade as deep as purple. We are told that it is the winter-cold that makes the leaves curl up into a cylinder, but sometimes one wonders. We know little about the nervous and sensory systems of plants. We can observe the reactions of the "insect-catching" group—the pitcher plants, fly-traps, sun-dews—and we are familiar with the varieties of sensitive plants. But what do we know of the reaction of plants to our interfering with, managing and controlling their sex lives and progeny? Who knows whether they may not begin, in revolt, to develop some kind of new, unknown poisons, worse than those they now have?

# Narcissus, Daffodil
## and Jonquil

## Narcissus poeticus; N. pseudo-narcissus;
## N. jonquilla

Never attempt to eat any bulbs "which lack the familiar odor of onions," says an authoritative book on edible wild plants.[1] It cites the narcissus, especially, as a highly suspicious bulb. It isn't as if we are going to start chewing on those sleek white or tan-skinned bulbs we bought from the flower shop; we aren't foraging in a wilderness. But the bulbs do lie around the house for a while before we get to planting them, they do resemble small misshapen onions and they could be picked up by a child and eaten.

The lovely flowers they produce are, like pussy willow and forsythia, the true harbingers, indeed the uplifting spirit, of spring. It seems intolerable that they must lie under a cloud of suspicion as dangerous. But they belong to the Amaryllis family, whose wild Easter lily has caused, by some unknown principle, poisoning of ani-

[1] Fernald and Kinsey, *Edible Wild Plants. op. cit.*

*Narcissus*

mals. And more importantly, the bulbs of narcissus, along with those of snowdrop and hyacinth, poisoned the livestock which were fed them during fodder shortages in World War II in Holland. They contain as yet unidentified alkaloids.

These daffy-downdillies, as they were termed in England a few centuries back, just as the cucumber was also called by a term I used to think my father had jocularly distorted—cowcumber—have been beloved flowers from the most ancient times and for the best reasons.

There is great confusion in identification of the plants—from the early writings of the Greeks to contemporary flower catalogues, unless botanical names are given in them. *Narcissus* is the name of the whole genus and its flowers have been found preserved in Egyptian tombs. Today so many hybrids are being developed for largeness of the bloom and variety of color that it is almost impossible to find any of the simple varieties unless you can discover an old farmhouse where the true, delicate, fragrant *Narcissus poeticus*—as I assume it to be—grows around the doorsteps. It is small in the blossom, with three, four or more white flowers with yellow eyes on each stalk, and is delightfully scented. The leaves are long, thin, tubular and, like the flower stalks of all these plants, as John Gerard says, "full of a slimie juice." In spite of what some flower catalogues state, to me the flowers called daffodils, jonquils, butter-and-eggs, and so on, are less fragrant, if fragrant at all, and tend more to pungency, like a daisy or a chrysanthemum; and they have rather flat, rush-like leaves, instead of tubular ones, sprouting from the bulb. The name jonquil comes through one or two languages from the Latin *juncus*, meaning "rush." And daffodil comes to us as a corruption of asphodel, the flower which covered the Elysian Fields.

Some of the charm of the original plant is still available in the indoor blooming "paper-whites" sold by florists for forcing in a bowl of pebbles and water. The fancy hybrids are merely for show as oversized blossoms which have little other character. The appeal of the old simple flower is described to perfection in the Homeric "Hymn to Demeter":

> *The Narcissus wondrously glittering, a noble sight for all, whether immortal gods or mortal men; from whose root a hundred heads spring forth, and at the fragrant odor thereof all the broad heaven above and all the earth laughed, and the salt wave of the sea.*

Pliny, resenting Ovid's invention of the myth of the origin of the plant from the death of the youth, Narcissus, in his *Metamorphoses*, wrote caustically that its name derived from *"Narce* which betokenneth nummednesse or dulness of sense, and not of the young boy *Narcissus,* as poets do feign and fable." That origin—numbness and dullness of the sense—ought to be warning enough against consumption of the bulbs. Culpeper, in his *Complete Herbal*, noted that "Given internally, in a small quantity, either in decoction or powder," the bulbs "act as a vomit, and afterwards purge a little." Gerard, writing earlier, had found more virtue in the viscosity of the juices to "consound and glew together very great wounds, yea and such gashes and cuts as happen about the veins, sinues, and tendons."

Those juices can provoke dermatitis in some people but little more is known about the toxic properties of the Narcissus family except that the bulbs are to be considered dangerous. They are placed by Dr. W. C. Muenscher in the same group as the most seriously poisonous of ornamental plants introduced into this country. There are instances of the bulbs being mistaken for leeks—washed, cooked and eaten, with the consequential poisoning of all concerned. But the poison is not without its prospects of

a more useful future. Some of the recent energetic research for new plant drugs has been directed towards these
daffodils and it is believed that compounds extracted from
the plant may prove useful in treating myasthenia gravis
and multiple sclerosis.

# Oleander

## *Nerium Oleander*

*I*ts very name, to say nothing of the sight of it, submerges me in some of my earliest memories—summer holidays on the Mississippi Gulf Coast: the hot sand and sandbars of the beach, the trolley tracks which ran the twenty-one miles along the shore from Pass Christian to Biloxi, paralleling the crushed oyster shell road down which each morning came the horse-drawn wagons of fruit, vegetable and fish vendors, which stopped at each house along the waterfront; and our house, huge, dim, airy, amid live oak trees, with mosquito bars affixed to every bed, and hedges of oleanders everywhere, growing like enormous, pungent, pretty weeds from the sandy loam. It is all gone now, replaced by modern air-conditioned hotels, motor courts, four-lane highways, restaurants, bars, gifte shoppes, real estate "developments"—all except some of the trees and the oleanders. The curious thing is that, though many more delicate and sophisticated plants—*Camellia japonica*, azalea, hibiscus, tall palms and tropical exotics—have been imported, the oleander persists in living and being loved.

Loved, that is, until something dreadful happens. For it can happen, if one is not aware of the danger, and

*Nerium Oleander*

it *has* happened wherever the oleander grows, which seems to be all over the world today. Where the climate is not warm enough, it is often cultivated in a tub indoors. But this was not always so. It is a native of the Asian continent. The "rose" of Ecclesiastes is interpreted by modern scholars as the oleander. Two of the ancient Greek names for it were compounds formed with "rose," in the same way that we often use rose as a synonym for flower. Because of its attractive foliage and flowers, and its stout adaptability, the oleander was long ago introduced into many lands as an ornamental shrub. Its ingratiating qualities are that it is evergreen, grows fast and will root, almost instantly it sometimes seems, from a slip stuck into rich, sandy soil.

The shoots come up in thick bunches from the roots and eventually, if the plant is happy, grow as high as twenty feet. All along the shoots are long, narrow, rich green leaves and the flowers, appearing at the ends of the shoots in clusters, are white, yellow, pink or red. Except in the Indian species, *Nerium odorum*, the flowers have little scent, but I have always felt that when hot sun falls on the shrubs (which is the way they prefer to live) an odor faintly like that of eucalyptus is evident.

As to that fragrant Indian oleander, however, I may as well quote Theophrastus, "In Gedrosia they say there grows a tree with a leaf like that of the bay, of which if the beasts or anything else ate, they very shortly died with the same convulsive symptoms as in epilepsy." He was not quite so negative about another species and remarked that its root, "administered in wine makes the temper gentler and more cheerful." These two kinds of oleander sound rather contradictory, but the comments seem to sum up the historical verdict that, up to the present, oleander's juices have been of service to man. Pliny reported that though its flowers were favorites for making chaplets: "It is a strange fact that, while its leaves are poisonous to quadrupeds, to man on the other hand, if rue is added and the mixture taken in wine, they are a protection against the poison of snakes. Sheep too and goats, if they drink water in which these leaves have been steeped, are said to be killed by it." Maybe one cannot be certain who would steep anything in water for sheep and goats, or why, but Pliny's statement that the plant is poisonous to quadrupeds would help to account for its family name, dogbane.

Mankind, however, is not to escape the oleander's toxin so easily. From Pliny again: "There is another kind of honey, found in the same district of Pontus among the people called Sanni, which from the madness it produces is called *maenomenon* [raving]. This poison is supposed to be extracted from the flowers of the oleanders which abound in the woods. Though these people supply the Romans with wax by way of tribute, the honey, because of its deadly nature, they do not sell." He reports poisoned honeycombs in Persia and Gaetulia and then raises the question which springs to our minds as well, "Yet it is wonderful that the bees, carrying poison in their mouths and working with it, do not themselves die."

Gerard had the oleander in his garden or house. But the plant seems little known in England.

One can realize some of oleander's potential dangers by reading the reports published by J. W. Harshberger concerning soldiers on field maneuvers. In one instance five men were making themselves a pot of barley soup and, not having a long-handled spoon to stir with, substituted a branch of oleander. All were poisoned by the soup. In another case, involving an army of French troops in Catalonia, the long smooth oleander branches, stripped of leaves, were used as skewers for roasting meat; three hundred men were poisoned and a number of them died.

The grim connotations of the yellow oleander's common name in the Hawaiian Islands—"be-still tree"—should now be evident. One or two of the fruits of the shrub (*Thevetia peruviana*) may prove to be fatal and on Oahu it is said to be the cause of more illness or death to man than any other poison.

The plant contains two cardioactive glycosides called nerioside and oleandroside, which cause reactions much like those of digitalis. Because these toxic substances are resinous compounds, they can be carried in the minute particles of smoke and therefore no part of the plant should be burned. If you trim it with hedge shears, don't throw the clippings, green or dried, on a fire. Along with affecting the heart as a depressant, the poisons act as a sedative to the whole body. Thus, we encounter a possibly more benign interpretation of "be-still tree."

These drugs, however, are not used at present in medicine and the shrub belongs to a family with a large number of poisonous members. Various species of hemp, vinca (or periwinkle) and dogbane are, with oleander, in the *Apocynum* family and provide many folk and official medicines. The most important member is the Asiatic "snakeroot" (not our familiar snakeroot, though so named for the same reasons), which has been used as an antidote for snakebites and as a sedative by the East Indians for three thousand years. Its scientific name is *Rauwolfia serpentina*; some species of *Rauwolfia* grow in all tropical regions and may share something of the virtues of *serpentina*. It was first reported to Western civilizations in the sixteenth century and, although other succeeding reminders of its properties were given to scientists, the plant was ignored by the West until 1947.

It was described briefly by Edson F. Woodward, as quoted by Margaret Kreig in *Green Medicine*: "*Rauwolfia serpentina*, from a distance, looks something like a small azalea. It has dark, glistening leaves and clusters of white to yellowish-pink flowers. Its berries are sparse and blue-black." Miss Kreig notes elsewhere, however, that one species in Peru grows to a height of a hundred feet and one in Rhodesia is only six inches high.

Suddenly this plant became the center of intense investigation by scientists, as well as of intense rivalry among the commercial drug manufacturers. The result, omitting the long story which led to it, was the discovery of reserpine, extracted from the roots, and today an important drug in the treatment of high blood pressure and mental illness.

Maybe this is rather far afield from oleander, but the two plants are of the same family: both depress the heart and both can cause death. Oleander will probably never attain the high medicinal glory of *Rauwolfia*, since it has no ancient tradition of folk remedies to vouch for or suggest its potential, but it still can be appreciated and enjoyed, if you just look at it and smell it, bearing in mind that it is poisonous.

# Pasque Flower

### *Anemone patens* or *pulsatilla*

*A* member of the crowfoot family (*Ranunculaceae*), almost all of which are in some degree poisonous, the pasque, or Easter, flower is usually grown in rock gardens or at the outer edges of a border, since its height is seldom more than six or seven inches. Its genus name, *Anemone*, should not lead one to confuse it, as its appearance certainly would not, with the more familiar anemones which are vari-colored and grow as tall as two or more feet. Its leaves are much like the foliage of carrots except that they are covered with silky gray hairs. The flowers are large and their colors shade from purple to pale blue, though *A. nemorosa* produces a white blossom and, as if in deference to such a blazon of purity, a lesser amount of poison.

The pasque flower (*A. patens*) is a native of Illinois and Wisconsin and the prairies stretching north and west; other similar varieties are native in England and parts of Europe. Its larger and apparently harmless relatives are widespread all over the world. Modern authorities consider that the Biblical "lilies of the field" were not lilies at all but anemones. The name means "windflower," a common designation for the plants, and despite Pliny's assertion that the flowers never open except when the wind blows, a more likely explanation of the name is the graceful swaying of the large bright blossoms in every gust of air.

"All the kinds of Anemones are sharp, biting the tongue, and of a binding facultie," says Gerard. Of the pasque flower specifically, a modern authority[1] reports that sniffing the crushed leaves or flowers has brought on headache, fainting and inflammation of the eyes. On the other hand, Culpeper, back in the seventeenth century, held that an ointment made from the herb would *help* inflammation of the eyes. And a second modern authority writes that homeopaths use it to *treat* nervous headaches, as well as for measles, asthma and other ailments.[2] Herbalists, homeopaths, unite and reach an agreement!

One thing is fairly certain, however; in some people the plant can produce dermatitis and if the juice gets into a scratch or cut, a sore may result. And in case any reservations remain as to the dangerous nature of this plant, let me quote Mrs. Leyel as to the rather contradictory actions of the poison secreted in the pasque flower: "Antispasmodic, diuretic, expectorant, emmenagogue, galactagogue, mydriatic, sedative, stimulant."

These diversified properties of the pasque flower are invested in an acrid yellow oil containing the alkaloid anemonine, which irritates and inflames the tissues of the body. A similar substance, anemenol, is contained in many of the pasque flower's relatives such as the buttercup or crowfoot (*Ranunculus*), or as they were once called, gold cups or butter-flowers.

Though I personally find their foliage and modest yellow flowers attractive, I don't know that anyone has cultivated the wild varieties (hybrids of many colors,

[1] Mary Thorne Quelch, *Herbs and How to Know Them* (London, Faber & Faber Ltd., 1946), p. 232.

[2] Mrs. C. F. Leyel, *Elixirs of Life* (London, Faber & Faber, Ltd., 1948), pp. 141–142.

grown from bulbs, are offered in catalogues) and they are left to their marshes and pastures, where they poison cattle and turn the milk bitter or even faintly red. "Pernitious herbes," warned Gerard, "whereof most are very dangerous to be taken into the body"; and he tells us that in his day beggars rubbed the juice of the plant into scratches to create sores as a visual plea for charity. Though Robert Browning spoke of them as "the little children's dower," in our own age we are cautioned by Mrs. Quelch: "Children should not be encouraged to handle buttercups, they are better left alone."

And, needless to say, that is equally true of the pasque flowers which may be growing, much more readily available to the children's hands, in your garden.

# *Poppy*

## *Papaver somniferum*

*T*here are poppies and poppies, all delightful but some with harmful juices in their veins. Since *Papaver somniferum* is the one which provides opium, it is not likely that you have it planted in your garden unless you are both a clever gardener and a law-breaker. And even if the plant should inadvertently sprout there from wind-borne seeds, unless you uproot it forthwith, you will still be breaking the law. For you cannot legally buy opium poppies, grow them, let them grow, or even move them from one place to another. The trouble is that though opium products are most important and necessary medicinal drugs, they are habit-forming.

The United States law has been in effect for some years and most people who grow poppies have what is called the Oriental (though the opium poppy is an oriental plant) and Iceland perennials or sow the annual California and Shirley types. But in out-of-the-way places where the annual opium poppy once grew, it may still be reseeding itself—in deserted fields or near abandoned gardens. Like most poppies, it is a rather handsome plant and has big, bluish green, tooth-edged leaves and large flowers ranging in color from blue-tinted white to reddish

*Papaver somniferum*

purple with a darker center showing at the base of the petals. It produces a seed capsule, large and smooth, from which, while still unripe, the milky juice called opium is expressed. The stems, too, as with other species, have this so-called "latex" and when poppies are cut for use in vases, the stems are usually cauterized over a flame to prevent the latex from seeping down into the water and causing the flowers to wilt and shatter.

If the recorded history of the opium or garden poppy (as distinguished from the red "corn poppy") goes far back, its unrecorded use goes even farther. Seeds have been found in the sites of the prehistoric Swiss Lake Dwellers. It had been used by the Assyrians and Babylonians as an aphrodisiac, and by the Egyptians as a narcotic. In times of the written word Hippocrates included it as one of his herbs. Dioscorides listed it as a poison but supplied therapeutic uses: "the leaves and heads boiled in water bring sleep. The decoction of these is also drunk as a remedy for sleeplessness. Finely powdered and mixed with groats, the heads make a good poultice for use against swellings and erysipelas. They must be pulverized while still green, formed into tablets, then dried and so stored for use."

Some scholars have claimed that this is the *nepenthe* which Helen gave to Ulysses in Book IV of the *Odyssey*:

> *But now it entered Helen's mind to drop into the wine that they were drinking an anodyne, mild magic of forgetfulness. Whoever drank this mixture in the wine bowl would be incapable of tears that day—though he should lose mother and father both, or see, with his own eyes, a son or brother mauled by weapons of bronze at his own gate. The opiate of Zeus's daughter bore this canny power. It had been supplied her by Polydamma, mistress of Lord Thôn, in Egypt, where*

*the rich plantations grow herbs of all kinds, maleficent and healthful.*[1]

In quoting this passage Theophrastus remarked that among these drugs Homer had placed *nepenthes*, "the famous drug which cures sorrow and passion, so that it causes forgetfulness and indifference to ills." It sounds very like opium.

But other writers claim the honor for hashish, henbane, mandrake or even bugloss. Theophrastus had already commented on "poppies," though not all were true members of the genus as we know it, but of one, the corn poppy (*P. rhoeas*), he said that it "is like wild chicory, wherefore it is even eaten: it grows in cultivated fields and especially among barley. It has a red flower, and a head as large as a man's finger-nail." This is the poppy which blows "in Flanders' fields."

Theocritus often mentioned poppies in his poems, sometimes citing only the color—as of the corn poppy— "the blood of poppy-posies," sometimes only their habit of growth in the fields, sometimes only their narcotic effect—"Lulling as poppies is your voice." Virgil, who was just as bucolic as Theocritus, particularly in his *Eclogues* and *Georgics*, frequently refers to the poppy, as in the first *Georgic*, "the poppies that draw death's drowsiness o'er them."

Students of the botany in the Bible give an interesting interpretation of the passage in Matthew 27:34, "They gave him vinegar to drink mingled with gall: and when he had tasted thereof, he would not drink." These scholars say the "vinegar" was sour wine and the "gall" was opium, explaining that the soldiers pitied his suffering and wished to give him something to relieve it. Jesus, in rejecting the drug which could have made him senseless of his agony,

[1] *The Odyssey*, trans. by Robert Fitzgerald (New York, Doubleday and Company Inc., 1961, 1963).

made a more heroic and noble gesture than he is usually credited with—merely rejecting a bitter drink.

The opium poppy had for centuries been used as a medicinal plant and as a "mysterious force" to help sustain the religious power of priests by Egyptians, Persians, Indians and Chinese. It was considered a remedy for earache, gout and erysipelas. Pliny gave a very plausible recipe for a cough syrup, a mixture of opium, honey and anise; and he explained the drug briefly: "Poppy juice however being copious thickens, and squeezed into lozenges is dried in the shade; it is not only a soporific, but if too large a dose be swallowed the sleep even ends in death."

As must already be evident, the plant had spread in the earliest times from Asia Minor through Greece and Rome and their colonies, and the Roman conquerors would probably have carried some knowledge of poppies, if not the seeds, through most of the rest of Europe and the British Isles. Even if they had not done this, the seeds were being introduced accidentally. The poppy's favorite site is sun-swept grain fields, and it has been said that it was an integral part of the worship of Ceres, Roman goddess of agriculture (whence "cereal"). Theocritus, at the end of his seventh "Idyll," plainly describes Demeter, the Greek prototype of Ceres, as holding in one hand "Cornsheaves, and in the other poppy-bunches." In the export shipments of grain from Asia Minor many poppy seeds inevitably went along to new parts of the world where the resulting plants at length became naturalized.

Still, in the West the opium poppy was generally regarded as only a therapeutic drug. Whether the expansion of its use as medicine—a use which cannot soon be dispensed with—to its use as an addictive drug can be attributed to a change—an advance—in technology, to a deterioration in Western culture and morals, to new social pressures, to all these or something more, perhaps no one can convincingly say. In the twelfth century Pseudo-Apuleius was prescribing it in the usual way: "For sleeplessness, take ooze of this same wort, smear the man with it; and soon thou sendest the sleep on him."

The suggestion in Dr. Short's *Herbal* for preserving chastity is not necessarily unusual, in view of the prevailing opinion that the continued use of narcotics acts to deprive the user of sexual potency, to say nothing of the fact that, if one has fallen into a deep sleep, one can hardly go about committing sexual acts; but the reference the doctor made *is* unusual. He wrote: "The monks, nuns, friars and hermits that would live chastely drink daily for twelve days together a drachm of [water lily] and syrup of poppies. This deprives the taker of all desire, inclination, and power of coition." At any rate, the most active ingredient in this recipe would be the water lily, which Dioscorides and, of course, Pliny, report as capable of rendering a person incapable of intercourse and procreation.

In *Othello* Shakespeare looked upon it, it seems, as no more than a soporific; in Iago's speech:

> . . . . *No Poppy, nor Mandragora*
> *Nor all the drowsie Syrups of the world*
> *Shall ever medicine thee to that sweete sleepe*
> *Which thou owd'st yesterday.*

As to uses of the poppies—the white opium poppy, and the black corn poppy—*Bancke's Herbal* advises, "For to provoke sleep, make a plaster of each of them or one of them with woman's milk and the white of an egg and lay it on the temples." However, the *Grete Herbal*, only a year later (1526), was slightly less cheerful about the beneficial effects of opium; only a grain of it "mortifieth all the wits of a man in such manner that he feeleth no pain and causeth him to sleep." It is still described as an anodyne, except for that suggestion in "mortifieth the wits." Crescentius was not quite so sanguine about it, saying it "makes you susceptible to colds and can kill you."

Culpeper reported that the opium poppy grew five or six feet high and in Ireland grew wild, but was cultivated in English gardens. "Opium," he wrote, "is nothing more than the milky juice of this plant, concreted into a solid form. It is procured by wounding the heads, when they are almost ripe, with a five-edged instrument, which makes as many parallel incisions from top to bottom; and the juice which flows from these wounds is the next day scraped off, and the other side of the head wounded in like manner. When a quantity of this juice is collected, it is worked together with a little water, till it acquires the consistence and colour of pitch, when it is fit for use." But, he goes on to say, it is to be used with great caution, as it is "a very powerful, and, consequently, a very dangerous medicine in unskilful hands" and frequently causes death.

The juice extracted from the unripe pod of the white poppy, the opium which was to trigger so many upheavals, small and large, contains more than twenty separate alkaloids. Small wonder that so many derivatives of opium have been developed. One of the earliest is laudanum, a tincture of opium invented and named by Paracelsus in the sixteenth century; in fact, he created *two* laudanums, presumably one more potent and costly than the other. Morphine was the first alkaloid to be isolated; the two other most important substances derived from opium are codeine and heroin. Some of the alkaloids act in ways contrary to the effects of others. Needless to say, all are dangerous.

But the fascination with the poppy was growing rapidly, though it was not directed at the beauty of the blossoms. In antiquity the use of opium was rather closely restricted to the priesthood, the sorcerers, the royalty and to its use as medicine. In modern times it has taken a major place in all levels of society, not simply as an indispensable drug of physicians and surgeons, but as a necessity to thousands of adults in their flight from the stress of reality and, most shockingly, to thousands of young people in their resistance to facing maturity and responsibility.

Information about its effects was slowly spreading and intriguing the down-trodden as well as the intellectuals. Until the rather recent interest in the hemp derivatives, opium was the exotic oriental drug par excellence. References to it began to appear more and more in Western literature and, as early as 1821, an English classic, Thomas De Quincey's *Confessions of an English Opium-Eater*, centered around the drug. An opera, *L'Oracolo* by Franco Leoni, which had a setting in San Francisco's Chinatown, a villain described as "keeper of an opium joint," and opium smokers in the chorus, was presented at the Metropolitan Opera House in 1915. London's Chinatown, Limehouse, was being described in Thomas Burke's stories during the same period. One of the extraordinary charlatans of our time, Aleister Crowley, who died in 1947, spent a lifetime in exploration of the occult, black masses and sex cults and, quite naturally, these narcotics turn up frequently in his writings. In the past decade the concern with opium derivatives and other drugs has accounted for a depressingly large portion of the fiction written by the young. An outstanding example from the drama is Jack Gelber's *The Connection*, whose theme is heroin and whose most gripping scene is one in which the author provided no words for the actor; it is a grim pantomime of a man giving himself a "fix."

Three murder cases which involved morphine as the agent of death are presented in Jürgen Thorwald's *The Century of the Detective*. Morphine was isolated in 1805 and its first known use for murder occurred in 1823, administered by Dr. Edmé Castaing.[2] Two more famous

---

[2] Thorwald, *Century of the Detective*, pp. 293–295.

cases, both once again involving medical men, occurred in New York later in that century, and are especially interesting because one of the homicidal doctors knew, he thought, how to use one poison to mask the effects of another and so commit the perfect crime. A young medical student, Carlyle Harris, on February 1, 1891, had murdered his secret wife, nineteen-year-old Helen Potts, by substituting a lethal amount of morphine in a capsule of the sedative she was taking. Dr. Robert W. Buchanan, who lived in Greenwich Village, was with friends when Harris's sentence was made public and declared that morphine poisoning was a likely means of getting away with murder. Just over a year later he put that theory to the test by killing his wife Annie with the drug and using a reagent to counteract the crucial evidence of morphine —dilation of the pupils of the eyes. The reagent was atropine drops (see *Atropa belladona*) but the crime did not go undetected.[3]

And as this book goes to press, the newspapers carry the story of the discovery of a wealthy eighteen-year-old girl's body in the trunk of a well-to-do young man's car. "He was booked for homicide," one paper reported, "charged with having injected a fatal dose of heroin."

It may be impossible to explain the increasing desire for taking narcotics, but some of the background causes may lie in the history of world trade. Contrary to most people's supposition, the use of opium did not originate with the Chinese but with the Arabs. Since alcohol is forbidden to the followers of Mohammed, what could be more natural than that they should turn to narcotics such as hashish and opium? Arabians spread the plant and its drugs through Persia and India. But in China the poppy

[3] *Ibid.*, pp. 324–335. The Harris case is treated, without Thorwald's chemical and scientific details, by Edmund Pearson in "The Sixth Capsule," included in *Murder at Smutty Nose*, Dolphin Books (New York, Doubleday & Company, Inc.).

was only a garden ornamental; it was not until the tenth century that it even became one of their medicines, a remedy for dysentery.

Still, opium was not produced in China until 1853, and until then, such quantities as were used were imported from India. The quantities, however, had been growing larger annually, for when the smoking of tobacco was prohibited in China in the seventeenth century, the populace simply took to smoking opium. Thousands of cases of opium began to pour into China from neighboring countries on ships of many flags. At length the Emperor Yung-Ching forbade the sale or smoking of opium, but at that late date to little effect. When the East India Company wished to import great shipments of opium from the British Colony India into China and was opposed by the government, the Opium War (1839–1842) broke out and finally, after eight years of warfare, the Chinese were forced to make the importation of opium legal. "Thus, the outlawed *Foreign Black Mud* was distributed in true gangster fashion all over the Chinese mainland, eventually destroying the power of the Chinese population to resist the commercial demands of the Western Powers," wrote Ernst and Johanna Lehner.[4] They also noted that in the 1930's the Japanese, having learned from this bit of history, smuggled heroin through Korea into China, their smuggling "aimed at breaking the Chinese will to resist their domination."

In the United States, where addiction has only become a problem in this century, the Bureau of Narcotics has, over the years, seemed more concerned with thoughts of self-preservation than by the problem of drugs, and the results of its actions and policies grow daily more evident and more costly, not merely in money, but in the declining

[4] Ernst and Johanna Lehner, *Folklore and Odysseys of Food and Medicinal Plants* (New York, Tudor Publishing Company, 1962), p. 110.

health of the nation, individually, morally and officially. What has resulted is not control of drugs but, in a sense, the multiplication of addiction and crime. The agency has removed distribution of opium derivatives from the hands of doctors and thereby turned it over to, or one might say, created, a vast underworld of dope racketeers, profiteers, and in turn a growing number of addicts who will commit any crime to get the money needed to pay for their fixes.

The "pusher," then, has not always been a grubby, faceless little man motivated only by financial gain, though that gain seems to have been always the dominant urge behind the pusher, individual, incorporated or official.

Meanwhile, enjoy the bright, gossamer flowers on the poppies you may have growing and leave the pods, opium type or not, untouched. The poppy seeds which are used to decorate and flavor foods are harmless. They have ripened, and opium comes from the unripe pod, which may by the way contain as many as 30,000 seeds.

# *Privet*

## *Ligustrum vulgare*

*T*hough it may not be our most handsome hedge plant, privet is certainly the most popular and widespread. It is, in fact, so widespread that since its introduction from Europe it has, in some eastern states, escaped from cultivation and begun to grow wild. When one looks at the straggly, almost defoliated, grime-covered plants set out, because of the privet's hardy nature, in city backyards, area-ways, neglected planting boxes and entry plots, one can hardly blame it for taking to the woods.

Given a soil made up of something more nourishing than acid soot and grime, however, the privet will flourish and amply repay, in rapid growth and pleasant foliage, its keeper. It is much like box in its leaves and adaptability to trimming, but the privet leaves are larger and duller and the meshing of cut branches is less compact—in fact, the whole plant appears coarser than the box. The one thing which is the same about them is the poison.

Privet must be clipped in the first years to produce a good dense hedge—a procedure calling for ruthless close shearing to prevent holes and thin spots—and the mature hedge can be very attractive. If garden space allows, the plants are also attractive in a free-growing

*Ligustrum vulgare*

state. They will grow up for eight or more feet and, if set against a fence, will droop their top branches over the outside in a green overflow which never reaches the ground. One sees them like this on the roads bordering many of the homes in Southampton, on Long Island, where they form excellent screens from prying eyes and blasting winds.

There is another common type which grows twice as tall as a weedy sort of multiple-trunked tree with leaves about four inches long. I knew that ligustrum was the name of this giant hedge plant long before I knew the botanical name for privet. I have looked out a second-story window in North Carolina upon the inner side of one of these plants which was using the house for support and have found the window frame filled with huge bunches of dusty, purple-blue berries, like grapes. The top of the tree went on up above my line of vision.

Just as the berries are attractive, so are the white flowers, which are borne in a cluster of racemes; but the odor, though sweet, is cloying and tinged with something faintly rancid or musky. Bees and flies like the blossoms. Birds, however, seldom eat the pretty berries. Children are not so selective; in Europe they have died from eating them. And, though hardly any person would be lured into eating the tough leaves, animals have done so, with sad results. In some parts of England the privet is called "blue poison."

# Snow-on-the-Mountain

## Euphorbia marginata

*W*hat beautiful names we have given to many plants which are poisonous—snow-on-the-mountain, star-of-Bethlehem, larkspur, bleeding heart, wake-robin, honeysuckle. It was surely done in tribute to their beauty alone, and in ignorance, until recent times, of their toxic properties. For other poisonous plants have common names (as well as their Latin botanical names) which act as warning signs: cursed crowfoot, death camass, deadly nightshade, locoweed, and so on. The English name of the order to which snow-on-the-mountain belongs—spurge—comes from an Old French word meaning to purge, and that describes one of the effects the plant has on the digestive organs. The botanical name of the order, *Euphoribiaceae*, is from the Latin name of an African plant and was bestowed on it by a Greek physician, Euphorbus. All of which is very roundabout and cosmopolitan!

Most spurges appear to have won, because of their ugly caustic qualities, many country names, especially in England, which are compounds using "devil," "adder," "snake," "boggart" and other such unpleasant words, though, strangely, some of the same plants may also be called "Virgin Mary's nipple." The association of the last name with the milky sap which oozes from cut stems of the spurges is apparent. However, the association of this white juice with that of other plants will lead to confusion. Many of the milkweeds (*Asclepias*) are edible if properly prepared, though any milkweed, eaten raw, may cause poisoning.

The spurges, wrote Culpeper, "abound with a hot and acrid juice, which, when applied outwardly, eats away warts and other excrescences." The oil from the seeds of one variety, he said, was good to kill lice on children's heads; and writing of another type, he said that it was "a strong cathartic, working violently by vomit and stool, but is very offensive to the stomach and bowels by reason of its sharp corrosive quality." This characteristic of the sap had long been confirmed by earlier writers. Of caper spurge (*E. lathyris*) Pseudo-Apuleius noted that it was good for "sore of the inwards," and, for warts and leprosy: "take heads of this same wort, sodden with tar, smear therewith."

The taste of the juice was described by Gerard, "I tooke but one drop of it into my mouth; which neverthelesse did so inflame and swell in my throte that I hardly escaped with my life." This particular spurge was *E. helioscopia*, whose juice mixed with honey, he says, is useful as a depilatory. As a purge the Euphorbia is, of course, a specific for "black choler" and is one of the remedies prescribed by Chanticleer's wife in Chaucer's "The Nun's Priest's Tale":

> . . . *take youre laxatives*
> *Of lauriol, centaure, and fumetere,*
> *Or elles of ellebor, that groweth there,*
> *Of catapuce, or of gaitris beryis.*

The "catapuce" is caper spurge, whose buds, it is said, were at one time bottled as a substitute for real capers.

Many of the thousands of spurges besides snow-on-the-mountain are dangerous or deadly—castor bean, croton, poinsettia, manchineel, crown of thorns and tung oil trees among them. Even the cassava, which like the manchineel grows mostly in Florida, and from whose roots the food products, cassava meal and tapioca, are made, belongs in this category; its poison is leached out before the products are edible. The poison in snow-on-the-mountain, and other similar low herbaceous spurges, is in the milky sap which, taken internally, acts not only as a purgative but as an emetic. Used externally, on the skin, the sap may cause inflammation and blistering, not by an allergen but by an acid. The poisonous principle in the sap is called euphorbon, whose caustic power, as has been indicated, is well known. The early herbalists were quite right in prescribing it for warts and the removal of hair. The ankles of horses were depilated and blistered after they had been working in grain fields in New York State where a variety of spurge was widespread. In Texas the sap of the pretty snow-on-the-mountain has been substituted, in branding stock, for the red-hot iron.

A large number of the spurges are native to the United States but most are rather unattractive and are looked upon as weeds. Snow-on-the-mountain, however, a native of the midwestern plains, is so attractive that it has been adopted as a garden ornamental and is cultivated all over the country. It thrives in almost any temperate climate, often sowing itself (it is an annual), and it reaches a height of two feet or more. The leaves are pale green with a white or creamy margin and the clusters of leaves, seen from a distance, appear to be white flowers which surround the flower. The flower itself is an insignificant sexual mechanism of no interest except that it functions. Other members of the Euphorbia family have been adapted from their wild state, or introduced from abroad, as ornamental plants for the border or as pot plants for the house or terrace. Among these are poinsettia (*E. pulcherrima*), cypress spurge (*E. cyparissias*), pencil tree ( *E. tirucalli*), candelabra cactus (*E. lactea*) and crown of thorns (*E. splendens*). All are to be looked upon as poisonous.

# Star-of-Bethlehem

## Ornithogalum umbellatum

*H*ow assiduously the Christian mind has worked to attach some religious sentiment to flowers by giving them such names as crown of thorns, Madonna lily, Easter lily, Michaelmas daisy, Christ's ladder, Judas tree, Virgin's bower and so on. In much the same way the ancient Greeks applied names of gods and heroes and their victims or beloveds to plants which have come down to us as daphne, hyacinth, narcissus (unless we believe Pliny and assume the youth was named for the flower and not vice versa), iris, andromeda, crocus, adonis, achillea and others.

There is a beautiful large purple and lavender flower which in my childhood I knew well and called, as people in the South still do, Maypop. Probably this name was attached to it because the ripe fruit, about the size of an egg and lemon-colored, would split with a faint pop when pressed, though some authorities have suggested the name may be a corruption of the Indian word, *maracock*. At any rate, most of the world knows the plant, if it knows it at all (its habitat is the hot climes of the Americas), as passionflower. Even its Latin botanical name is *Passiflora,* and a story tells that missionaries who found it in South

*Ornithogalum umbellatum*

America used it to demonstrate the Passion of Jesus to the natives, using the petals as the apostles, the filaments as the crown of thorns, the stamens as the wounds, etc. While one wonders how many converts they made with this sort of hortico-sermonizing, the plant *was* probably named in this way. When I learned the true name of the plant, I imagined, in my innocence, that the fruit would inspire passion. But enough—the Maypop *can* be eaten safely but the star-of-Bethlehem can be poisonous.

I say "can be" because, though we would all be wise to avoid eating any part of it on the basis of reports from

United States authorities, it is known that people of the East, Asia Minor and parts of Europe have used the bulbs as food. But as has been noted in reference to the castor bean plant, which the Javanese enjoy eating, the conditions of poisoning vary. Cooking would destroy the poison, and it is conceivable that people could eat the bulbs boiled or roasted (they taste like chestnuts, I've read), or after roasting, they could be ground into a flour.

Star-of-Bethlehem may have got its name as much from geographic as religious associations. It is a wild plant, extremely hardy in varied soils and climatic situations, and grows densely across fields in Palestine and Syria. Once introduced into other lands it promptly escaped from cultivation and reverted happily to its wild state, as we have it in this country. Its flower seems to me scarcely pure white enough to represent a chaste religious symbol. It is star-like, but its whiteness is rather diluted with the color of a green vein which runs down the middle of the back of each perianth. Even so, despite its poison and greenish-whiteness I rather like it.

The Latin name, *Ornithogalum*, means roughly "bird's milk" and that name continues today in German and Italian—*vogelmilch* and *latte d'uccello*. However, birds do not give milk like cows and goats; could this have been a euphemism? We find it under a variant name in the Bible (Kings II, 6:25) as a high-priced food in time of famine, "And there was a great famine in Samaria: and, behold, they besieged it, until an ass's head was sold for fourscore pieces of silver, and the fourth part of a cab of dove's dung for five pieces of silver." Bird's milk—dove's dung. It is called by the latter name in Samaria. As a corollary, let us look at a fragment of a poem by Abraham Cowley:

*The next akin, a flower which Greeks of old,*
*From excrements of birds, descended, hold,*

> *Which Britain, nurse of plants, a milder clime,*
> *Gentilely calls "The Star of Bethlehem."*

The bulbs of the plant contain the alkaloid, colchicine, whose uses have been discussed in connection with the autumn crocus. But this poison, in its non-useful phase, has killed not only livestock but children who have eaten the bulbs of the star-of-Bethlehem.

# Tobacco

## *Nicotiana species*

*M*ost gardeners, anxious to avoid sullying the esthetics of their concern with any taint of commercialism, speak of "flowering tobacco" or, scientifically, of Nicotiana. All the tobaccos flower, of course, but there are many species besides the well-advertised, fortune-producing *Nicotiana tabacum* from which cigars, cigarettes, snuff, etc., are made. Tobacco belongs to that distinguished family, *Solanaceae*, some of whose members are black nightshade, henbane, belladonna, mandrake and the deadly jimsonweed. It is a native of this hemisphere, but whether of the United States or regions to the south is uncertain. At any rate, Columbus noted it on his island voyages and it was found on the North American continent when later explorers arrived.

Gerard, who grew two varieties in his garden, called it "henbane of Peru," following his major source, Rembert Dodoens, and he called yellow henbane "English tobacco," not only because of its family connections but because some people smoked it instead of tobacco, "to small purpose or profit, although it doth stupifie or dull the sences, and cause that kind of giddines that Tabaco doth, and likewise spitting." Since tobacco had become a marvelous

*Nicotiana*

panacea by this time, as Gerard had remarked of other new and foreign herbs (goldenrod, for example), its virtues were boundless. It could be used to relieve migraine, gout, toothache, insomnia, dropsy, ague, catarrh, colds, rheumatism, deafness, tumors, carbuncles, burns and wounds of guns or poisoned arrows. In this decade of the 1900's I particularly relish his report of medicines made from tobacco "against the old and inveterate cough, against asthmaticall or pectorall griefs, all of which if I should set downe at large, would require a peculiar volume."

This tobacco was the commercial variety, undoubtedly, and not the kind which finds a welcome home in gardens. The commercial type, as anyone knows who has seen the fields in North Carolina and other parts of the country, or even the advertisements showing the huge cured leaves, is not for the flower garden. Other varieties which grow in tall spikey clumps, with small leaves and trumpet-like flowers of white or faint pink are favorites for the ornamental border. They mingle well in a mixed selection of cut flowers. Even more notably, the blooms on the simple original varieties open in early evening and fill the air, all through the night, with a delicious, delicate scent which has no resemblance to the odor of tobacco smoke. The popularity of the plant is demonstrated—and perhaps the reasons for its popularity obviated—by the development of many hybrids, of varying colors, heights and habits, which open the furled cap of each flower-funnel with the morning sun, as presumably all *good* plants do.

Well, alas, the commercial type as well as the fragrant, graceful garden type and all their wild relatives, contain the best known of all toxic alkaloids—nicotine. It is, in mild quantities, absorbed by human beings in fumes and juices from the cured leaves; but in its pure state, concentrated by distillation, it is deadly. Jürgen Thorwald details the rather horrid story of the Count Bocarmé who, in 1850, imported bales of tobacco and patiently worked to distill nicotinic acid from the cured leaves. Then, with the help of his wife, he forced the acid down her brother's throat in the hope of committing the perfect crime and inheriting money. The crippled brother expired almost instantly but the crime was woefully bungled.[1]

Nicotine, of course, is lethal only in large concen-

[1] Thorwald, *op. cit.*, pp. 296–306.

trated doses. The amount absorbed by smokers, chewers or sniffers of tobacco is small—usually—and the harm which it is claimed is done may not be caused by nicotine. Nicotinic acid, as has been noted earlier, is one of the components of multiple-vitamin pills. Nicotine is also a major substance in modern liquid insecticides. I recall the distant days when, before the commercial bug-killers, snuff was the handy and effective weapon against insects which might sap the strength of tomato plants and other vegetables.

The symptoms of nicotine poisoning are well known, in a mild form, to all users of tobacco—trembling, stupor, variable pulse, heart palpitations, depression. The more violent forms, brought on by consumption of the plant *Nicotiana*, are suffered mostly by incautious or starving animals and, since they include retching, bloating, diarrhea, etc., are not pleasant. One doesn't have to suffer these symptoms, of course, if one has a Count Bocarmé to administer an almost instant death with the pure fluid.

Luckily, as you might imagine, the leaves are bitter—even rabbits won't eat them—and many animals are spared thereby. But flowers of the garden variety are lovely and fragrant—it must be good to eat, a child might think.

# *Yew*

Japanese: *Taxus cuspidatus;*

English: *T. baccata;*

American: *T. canadensis*

*T*he "baleful yew," as Virgil called it in his second
*Georgic*, is a somewhat gloomy, though beautiful, evergreen shrub or small tree, and its dangerous qualities have
been known from ancient times. Theophrastus, in the
earliest surviving study of plants, wrote, "they say that, if
beasts of burden eat of the leaves they die," and Dioscorides, echoed later by Pliny, reported on the poisonous
nature of the plant, adding that even to rest under the
yews in a certain section of France was to tempt fate.
Much later in England, Culpeper noted that the leaves,
if distilled, produced "the most active vegetable poison
known in the whole world, for in a small dose it instantly
induces death." This warning had been voiced many centuries earlier by Nicander in his poem on poisons, *Alexi-
pharmaca*: "See that you do not pluck the dangerous pine-
like Yew of Oeta: it is the giver of lamentable death."

And yet the yew has always aroused veneration or

*Taxus cuspidatus*

strong attachment in Western mankind. The first no doubt sprang from the poisonous properties of the plant and its ability to live for hundreds of years. In England there is a huge yew tree in a churchyard in Hampshire which is over a thousand years old, one in Derbyshire close to two thousand years old, and in Perthshire one somewhere near three thousand years old, to mention only the senior members of the family. One explanation for the prevalence of large old yews near churches is that the early Fathers' desired to have them nearby to cite as symbols of immortality. An anonymous Gaelic poem of the twelfth century notes the association:

> *Little yew tree, yewy one,*
> *in churchyards you abound.*

A more likely reason for their presence beside churches is that the churches were built upon the ruins of pagan temples, as happened in the Roman empire, and in Mexico and Peru. The yew was revered by the Druids, along with mistletoe, and thought to be sacred to the moon. In the Greco-Roman culture as well, it was sacred to Artemis-Diana, the moon-goddess, and to Hecate (Diana-of-the-crossways), the goddess of witches. The three witches in *Macbeth*, who may well have been Druids, but who indeed have a scene with Hecate in the play, worked their charm by chanting:

> *Gall of goat; and slips of yew*
> *Sliver'd in the moon's eclipse.*

The poison which killed Hamlet's father may have been yew; the Ghost tells the Prince of Denmark:

> *Upon my secure hour thy uncle stole,*
> *With juice of cursed hebenon in a vial,*
> *And in the porches of mine ears did pour*
> *The leperous distilment.*

What was hebenon? Some scholars have suggested that it was yew, drawing upon corollaries with the word "hebon" for yew, which other Elizabethans had used, and with the German *Eiben* for "yew"; a second group, apparently using assonance as their argument, has offered ebony or henbane as the plant.

However that mystery may be resolved, it is known that yew was much employed by witches and magicians but it shared the classic dichotomy of most medicinal plants—it was also valuable as a protection against their spells. It could be used for evil or for good.

Our fondness for it is easily attributable to its endurance, its evergreen feather-like foliage, its bright red berries, its adaptability to pruning into hedges or topiary ornaments. Certainly its wood is lasting, for the oldest wooden weapons so far discovered—from the Paleolithic Age—were made of yew. The plant grows as a tree or a shrub, depending upon the variety, and has rather short dark green leaves, flattened rather than needle-shaped, as those of pines, spruce and hemlock are, and arranged on each side of the stem, as Kingsbury says, "like the slats of a closed Venetian blind." The underside of the leaves has a yellowish cast. The yellow flowers develop into pretty red ovoid "berries" rather than into cones, as other conifers do. Inside each berry is a single seed. Since the plant is dioecious—that is, the male and female organisms are borne on separate plants—only the female yew has these arils ("berries").

Culpeper says, "the berries are surrounded with a sweet juicy matter," and that this pulp and the flowers and roots are the only harmless parts of the plant. The seed, the leaves, the bark, and the wood contain an alkaloid called taxine, which weakens the heart and, if consumed in quantity, stops it completely.

The English yew, which has been introduced into the South, is reported to have killed many men and animals; the Japanese yew, more hardy and introduced into the northern regions, is hardly less dangerous. Nor, to avoid any charge of chauvinism, is our own American yew, commonly known as ground hemlock, any less poisonous. Ground hemlock should not be confused with the innocent hemlock tree, as it frequently is in the seedling stages, or the water hemlock. On the West Coast there grows a native variety of yew (*T. brevifolia*) which, upon analysis, yielded no alkaloids, but it is still under suspicion.

*Intruders*

# Deadly Nightshade

## Atropa belladonna

*I*f the common English name is not enough to warn you against this plant, then maybe the scientific one, in combination with it, will do so. *Atropa* is named for one of the three Fates of Greek mythology—Atropos, who cuts off the thread of life. *Belladonna* (Italian: "beautiful lady") —well, that isn't enough to erase the blot; it's just because the ladies of Venice used its juices to enhance their beauty. Mattioli in his commentaries on Dioscorides stated that they applied it to their eyes to dilate them and make them sparkle, and others held that the red sap was used as a cosmetic. At least Mattioli was right about the nature of the drug in deadly nightshade; anyone who has had his eyes examined by an oculist may recall that it was belladonna drops which dilated his pupils so that his vision was diffuse for some hours afterward.

The nightshade family (*Solanaceae*) is both large and very unusual. It includes a great many ornamentals, a great many delicious vegetables, and a great many poisonous plants, several of which will be discussed in this particular section. This present member, *Atropa belladonna*, was introduced into the United States from the Middle Eastern countries as a drug plant and in the years

*Atropa belladonna*

since its first cultivation for medicinal purposes here, it has "escaped" and is now found growing wild, naturalized in some of the eastern states.

It is a tall, ugly perennial herb, growing from a fleshy root as high as six feet, and dividing into three, perhaps four, branching purplish stems a little above the ground. The leaves are dull green, the flowers, which are bell-shaped and dingy purple with touches of green or yellow, droop from short stems in the axils, and all of the plant has an unpleasant odor. A plant of "a dismal aspect," said Culpeper. The flowers mature into berries, first green, then red, and finally, when ripe, black, and these are filled with a very sweet, inky, violet juice.

The classic writers spoke of this plant as mandragora (a close relative) and one cannot distinguish between the two in many instances. By the great age of herbalists, however, deadly nightshade had acquired a special reputation quite different from that of mandrake. Gerard warns (and before him Lyte did so too, calling it "this naughtie and deadly plant") against *Atropa belladona*:

> *Banish therefore these pernitious plants out of your gardens, and all places neere to your houses, where children or women with child do resort, which do oftentimes long and lust after things most vile and filthie; and much more after a berry of a bright shining blacke colour, and of such great beautie, as it were able to allure any such to eate thereof.*

Gerard also supplies a cautionary case history of the effects of "a plant so furious and deadly": "It came to passe that three boies of Wisbich in the Isle of Ely did eate of the pleasant and beautifull fruit thereof, two whereof died in lesse than eight houres after that they had eaten of them."

Even Culpeper, who was loath to say anything bad about a plant, had to admit that it "bears a very bad character as being of a poisonous nature. It is not good at all for inward uses." And, unless my modern reprint of his book is abridged, he failed, at least this one time, to assign to the plant its proper governance by astrological powers.

Older herb-doctors—witches as one might say—knew a thing or two which the scientific herbalists did not. We may react properly to Shakespeare's trio of witches in *Macbeth* as they chant on the stage, but if we consider coolly, we think of those ludicrous ingredients they boiled —eye of newt, toe of frog and so on. But today we know that toad skin provides a potent hallucinatory drug called bufotenin.[1] But Macbeth himself, if we are to believe Buchanan's *History of Scotland* (1582), was not so naive about plant drugs; when the Danes were invading, he made a truce, gave them wine spiked with "dwale" (belladonna) and had the whole army slaughtered in its drugged state. A pity he or Lady Macbeth didn't know about it or have something like it to use when they did away with their king, Duncan!

Still, witches persist, and one of their most useful herbs was deadly nightshade. Legends also persist, related to the plant—one, that the devil owns and tends it constantly and can only be lured from it on certain nights and then only by a black hen; and another, that it is the "apple of Sodom." So far as is known the witches had three formulae for their flying ointments. The recipe for the first was recorded by Reginald Scot (*Discoverie of Witchcraft*, 1584): "The fat of young children, and seeth it with water in a brasen vessel, reseruing the thickest of that which remaineth boiled in the bottome, which they laie up and keepe, untill occasion serueth to use it. They put hereunto Eleoselinum, Aconitum, Frondes populeas, and Soote."

The other two ointments call for the following ingredients:

[1] Margaret B. Kreig, *Green Medicine. The Search for Plants That Heal* (New York, Rand McNally and Company, 1964).

> *(1) Water parsnip, sweet flag, cinquefoil, bat's blood, deadly nightshade, and oil.*
>
> *(2) Baby's fat, juice of water parsnip, acon-ite, cinquefoil, deadly nightshade, and soot.*

Very likely the water parsnip in these was really hemlock. The deadly nightshade would cause excitement and pos-sibly delirium, and coupled with aconite, would produce irregular action of the heart, which "in a person falling asleep produces the well-known sensation of suddenly falling through space," could result in a sensation of flying through the air.[2]

If anyone should scoff at these recipes as medieval superstitions, he might be willing to do serious research into them, as others have done. In recent years Dr. Will-Erich Peuchert concocted a salve from an original witches' formula and with some associates put it to the test. It worked; in their day-long sleep they flew and danced and took part in orgies.[3]

Perhaps in actual practice some of these salves were used more as love ointments than as flying ointments, since they could easily render a female (or male) helpless in the orgies of the Witches' Sabbath. In pagan times the plant belonged not to Satan but to Hecate, the goddess of witches. Nightshade was naturally one of the herbs the witch in Ben Jonson's song had been gathering. In fact, the plant was called "enchanter's nightshade," in tribute to that great sorceress, Circe. Michael Drayton, in his *Nymphidia*, refers to witchcraft, "She nightshade straws to work him ill."

One writer on poisons has written of deadly night-shade, giving his source only as "a Prussian pastor," that

---

[2] Margaret Alice Murray, *The Witch-Cult in Western Europe* (Oxford, Oxford University Press, 1921), see Appendix V, by Prof. A. J. Clark, pp. 279–280.

[3] Kreig, *op. cit.*, p. 93.

in the seventeenth century the Lithuanians had "a plant which they call *maulda* and when they owe money to someone, they find means of introducing it into his drink. Whoever receives this plant into his body must die; the whole pharmacopeia cannot help him."[4]

But accidental poisoning, rather than murder, by deadly nightshade is more frequent and more usually involves children, who are attracted to the black shiny fruit, the size of a small cherry, and are, of course, pleased by its sweet taste. Gerard's report of two boys in the sixteenth century (in which account he includes other cases) has already been quoted. Of the many actual cases in our present century which are recorded in non-technical literature, we can cite one from London in 1916, in which three children ate berries of the plants growing in the public park (the gardener was not aware of their poisonous qualities), and one in 1921 which resulted in the death of a child, with the coroner stating that he had known of four similar instances. The fact that these incidents date back over forty years is of no relevance; reports of poisoning by plants are not often widely circulated in the popular press and most accounts are buried in medical journals.

In a few words, the effects of belladonna are narcotic, diuretic, sedative and mydriatic (causing dilation of the pupils of the eyes). With his characteristic delight, Schenk details the symptoms: "The victim [is] very cheerful and lively. . . . laughs and dances. . . . sees nonexistent figures. . . . hears music and sounds when there is complete silence all around him." He mentions also hysterical crying, convulsions, hallucinations, incoherent speech, delirium, as well as rapid respiration, decreased temperature and paralysis of the lungs. At this last stage, if the amount of poison swallowed is large, death results.

[4] Gustav Schenk, *The Book of Poisons*, trans. by Michael Bullock (New York, Rinehart and Company, Inc., 1955), p. 38.

The agent of these physiological and psychological reactions is, of course, the alkaloid in the deadly nightshade. From this plant, in 1883, atropine was isolated, though for many years it was spoken of simply as belladonna. It is a drug of great potency and only minute amounts are used medicinally. Because of its effect on the pupils of the eye, it is invaluable in ophthalmic operations. As this application of it might suggest, it acts on the involuntary muscles, paralyzing their nerve endings, and for this reason it is also useful in liniments and for asthma. It is widely grown as a crop for plant drugs.

Deadly nightshade is one of the plants currently being more deeply researched by scientists for new uses and derivatives which can benefit the human race. This serious attention it shares with several other members of its family, which are here considered in later pages as weeds. For their medicinal blessings, let us be thankful to these weeds, and even as we yank them out of the ornamental border and refrain from dosing ourselves with the raw foliage or berries, say, perhaps, a silent "God bless."

# Indian Hemp

## Cannabis sativa

*T*hough lovers of certain things, such as rope and illusions, might do so, no lover of gardens would think of planting or nurturing Indian hemp. Still, it could very easily appear in the flower beds and no one, except those lovers of "certain things" would call it anything but a rank weed. It is an annual, a member of the nettle family and resembles the stinging nettle in its gray-green hairy stems, its habit of blooming and its coarsely toothed leaves, and will grow in a season from three to ten feet in height. Its leaves are palmate, made up of five to seven rather narrow leaflets, and its flowers, small, green or maybe faintly yellowish, are unisexual. The male, or staminate, flower sprouts from the joints between leaves and stalk in panicles; the female, or pistillate, flower, looking like a seed already in a hairy sheathing leaf, grows in a spikey cluster, also from the angles of leaf and stem.

Since this unattractive plant is a native of India, one may well ask why it is widespread over this country. The reason is that it is, though not only ugly but dangerous, a useful plant. For centuries rope has been made from the fibers in the stems and the plant was introduced into many countries as a commercial crop for rope making. Even

*Cannabis sativa*

without such intentional introduction, Indian hemp would very likely have spread across the world, for the waste, to which the seeds clung after separating the fiber, was used as packing material and would have transported them to all countries to which merchandise was shipped from the Orient. This proposition is easily substantiated by observing the prevalence of Indian hemp colonies around railway unloading platforms in this country. Vacant lots in large cities have been discovered densely inhabited by a tall growth of hemp. And anyone who has ridden over the bridges across the Mississippi or Missouri Rivers will have seen vast stands of the plant covering the deserted bottom lands. It has been said that thousands of acres of it grow along these rivers.

In addition to hemp's value in the production of cordage, twine and coarse fabrics, its crushed seeds yield a useful oil. They are also included in mixtures of bird seeds, another cause of the spread of the weed. Furthermore, the narcotic properties of the whole plant have proved of value to medicine and when they are imported from the East they arrive in small packages made up of leaves, flowers and seeds glued together by the sticky exudation of resinous secretions. Thus, the plant could have been spread worldwide in other ways than planned introduction.

Tincture of the drug obtained from hemp is included in the United States Pharmacopoeia; the poison is usually spoken of as a resinoid, though its components have recently been isolated. Medicinally it can be employed, not only to induce sleep and reduce pain, but to treat gout, rheumatism, neuralgia and ailments of the kidneys and the urethra.

Though some have suggested the fruit of the jujube tree as the food of the Lotos-eaters among whom Ulysses almost lost some of his crew, is not hemp an excellent candidate?

> . . . *those who ate this honeyed plant, the Lotos,*
> *never cared to report, nor to return: they longed*
> *to stay forever, browsing on that native bloom,*
> *forgetful of their homeland.*[1]

These Lotos-eaters lived in Libya, a very likely and abundant source of hemp.

In his history of the *Persian Wars* (I, 202) Herodotus reported on the Scythians who lived near the Araxes

[1] *The Odyssey*, trans. by Robert Fitzgerald (New York, Doubleday & Company, Inc., 1961, 1963).

River: "They have also a tree which bears the strangest produce. When they are met together in companies they throw some of it upon the fire round which they are sitting, and presently, by the mere smell of the fumes which it gives out in burning, they grow drunk, as the Greeks do with wine. More of the fruit is then thrown on the fire, and, their drunkenness increasing, they often jump up and begin to dance and sing." Elsewhere he says the Thracians made garments of hemp, which closely resembled linen, and gave themselves "vapor baths" by throwing hemp seed on hot coals underneath a tent of felt.

The effects of Indian hemp on the human body, taken into it by eating or drinking, have been known for over three thousand years, certainly in its native habitat, Asia. Smoking was a practice among the Orientals long before the tobacco pipes of the American Indians were discovered by the first explorers of this continent; they puffed the fumes of the dried leaves or flowers as only one of the stimulating uses which they put the plant to.

They made an intoxicant from the resin which exudes from the leaves. One way of collecting this resin was for men, covered in leather garments, to run through the plantations of hemp, after which the gummy substance was scraped from the leather. Another was to roll the leaves between carpets—the undersides, not the pile—and scrape off the resin afterward. This collected deposit is called *charas* or *churrus*. The dried leaves of hemp were used to make a drink called *bhang, sidhee* or *subjee* or to concoct a sweetmeat called *majun*. A recipe for *bhang* appears in Burton's translation of *The Thousand Nights and a Night,* though it would appear to be a sweetmeat rather than a drink.[2]

---

[2] The authorities I have consulted do not always agree in their definitions of the oriental words and I, having no knowledge of either the languages or the narcotics, have made no attempt to clarify them in such a limited work as this.

> *'Tis composed of hemp leaflets, whereto they add aromatic roots and somewhat of sugar, then they cook it and prepare a kind of confection which they eat, but whoso eateth it (especially an he eat more than enough) talketh of matters which reason may in no wise represent.*

Élie Réclus, reporting on the use of hashish (the Arabian word for hemp products) in human sacrifices, wrote that the victims, to be pleasing to the deity, must go to their death voluntarily. "To this end they were given hashish to drink and on the day of the expiatory sacrifice their courage was kept up by an extra large ration of hashish. In a state of drunken ecstasy the victim then presented himself at the altar, where his throat was cut so that the Earth drank his blood." The drug was also used in India on widows at the *suttee* so that they would willingly be burned with their husbands' corpses.

Though the Asians did not ignore the medicinal properties of the plant at the expense of its stimulating qualities, in northern Europe in earlier times Indian hemp was not at all esteemed for its virtues of bestowing exaltation, dreams, and illusions, but only for its ability to heal. In the Middle Ages the Welsh had a recipe for curing wounds with hemp leaves. In the same period it was prescribed to make hair grow. Culpeper, much later, stated that it was good for the hot or dry cough, jaundice, gallstones, diarrhea, colic, worms, gout and other diseases, but warned that "too much use of it dries up the seed for procreation." In Mexico a poultice made of the leaves soaked in alcohol is a remedy for rheumatism.

In Morocco hemp is called *kif* and it figures in some of the fiction written in recent years by Paul Bowles. The Algerians made a confection called *madjound* out of honey and the powdered resin. In her cookbook, Alice B. Toklas included a recipe for hashish fudge which she got from Brian Gysen and which, she says, "anyone could whip up on a rainy day." It is a confection of spices, dates, figs, sugar and nuts, chopped, mixed, dusted with pulverized hemp leaves, and rolled into a cake. With disarming slyness, she recommends it as "an entertaining refreshment for a Ladies' Bridge Club or a chapter meeting of the DAR" and adds that, though there may be some difficulties in getting the leaves, it grows everywhere and in the Americas "has been observed even in city window boxes."

In the thirteenth century Marco Polo journeyed from Venice across the Asian continent to China and in his account of these travels he narrated the story of a Sheik, known as "the old man of the mountain," who lived near the borders of Persia. This man had devised an ingenious scheme for accomplishing his wishes, especially if he wished to commit a murder. In his palace he kept a company of young men to whom he would feed hashish; in their drugged sleep they would be transported to a beautiful harem of lovely women and they were informed that this was Paradise. But when they eventually found themselves back with the Sheik, they could only long for their lost Paradise. The Sheik, by this sort of brain-washing, organized these men into a band of murderers who would do his commands in order to reach Paradise. They were called *hashishin* ("hashish-eaters") and from the name has come our English word, assassin. Which stretches a bridge of hemp from the medieval era to our contemporary youth.

For Indian hemp, the mother plant of so many potions, pastes, candies, remedies and smoking materials under so many international names, is plain marijuana, better known to its users as "reefer," "weed," "tea," "stick," "pot" and a host of everchanging names to indicate the In status of the speaker. The popularity of marijuana, principally in cigarettes and among the young, has mounted alarmingly in the last few decades and, though its defenders point out that it is not habit-forming, others assert that its continued use leads to a desire for more potent narcotics which *are* addictive.

The alkaloids in hemp are most potent in the female plant, but the strength is also conditioned by the climate —the warmer the climate the stronger the poisons. They affect the higher nerve centers and produce a feeling of exaltation and an intensification of sensations. If continued, the use of the drug causes hallucinations, mental confusion, and finally, depression and deep sleep. Since marijuana slows down the heartbeat, it might, if taken to excess, cause death. The lower animals are apparently more rational in one respect than human beings—they almost never consume hemp in any form.

With a view to controlling the spread of such a dangerous narcotic plant, the government has prohibited the commercial production of hemp since 1955 and now requires that the seeds added to bird-seed mixtures be sterilized. Still, the weed is everywhere and teen-agers everywhere, it seems, smoke it.

Many plants are called hemp because they resemble Indian hemp in appearance and also furnish fiber for rope, twine and tow sacks, but they belong to different families. One of these, black Indian hemp (*Apocynum cannabinum*), an American native of the dogbane family, grows throughout this country and is of some interest. Unlike true hemp, it is a perennial of only moderate height, with smooth, oblong leaves. Its flowers, though also greenish white, bloom at the top of the stalks, and the thistle-like seeds are borne in long thin follicles. A more fascinating distinction is that the flowers hold a nectar which attracts insects to the corolla which then bends inward when touched, imprisoning the insects beneath the sensitive scales within. The fiber of this plant is used in California for twine, fishnets, lines and other similar products. The juice, like that of Indian hemp, is milky and poisonous; it contains a glycoside, symarin, which is related to the digitalis group of cardiac drugs. In spite of its toxic potency—grazing stock have died from eating small quantities of it—it has important medicinal value and possibilities. Years ago, when President Harrison suffered a severe heart attack and was not helped by digitalis, an extract of black Indian hemp brought him back to health.

# Hemlock

*Cicuta maculata*, water hemlock;

*Conium maculatum*, poison hemlock

$O$ne of the quartet of great ancient poisons (the others being hellebore, aconite and nightshade), hemlock has fascinated people for centuries by reason of its uses for good or evil and its disguises which trap the unwary. This plant, however, is not the beautiful conifer, the hemlock tree. To say that it belongs to the parsley-carrot family (*Umbelliferae*, "bearing umbels") is enough to warn of the ease with which it can be mistaken in the early stages of its growth for a harmless relative such as parsley, carrot, parsnip or Queen Anne's lace. By many it is accorded the title of most virulent poisonous plant in our part of the globe, where in one or another species and variety it grows from coast to coast.

The water hemlock is our native species and, as its name suggests, prefers a wet situation—damp meadows, pastures, creek banks, marshy thickets, moist ditches. In its full growth the perennial reaches a height of seven feet with compound leaves, serrated, rather like carrot tops. The stems are frequently spotted with purple, and the tiny

*Conium maculatum*

white flowers appear on compound umbels. The roots just below the stem are thick and grow in a clump like dahlia roots, and when cut or broken smell like parsnip or carrot. The taste also, on the evidence of those who have survived the experience, is rather like that of those two vegetables. As an indication of its reputation, it has earned such common names as cowbane, snakeroot, beaver poison and false parsley.

In his book Dr. Harshberger has quoted a letter to him from a Pennsylvania physician, which was accompanied by specimen roots which turned out to be water hemlock. "Yesterday, March 30 (11 to 12 P.M.) Chester Mulhollen, aged 8, Willard Mulhollen, aged 10 and Harold Fun aged 9 mistook these tubers for artichokes. They ate of them for about half an hour, consuming I suppose about as much as I mail to you. All three became suddenly ill a few minutes after they stopped eating. Chester M. started toward the house about 100 feet distant and fell in the door in a convulsion, never regaining consciousness. Harold F. dropped where he was in a convulsion. Willard M. became ill a few minutes later, and acted exactly like the others. . . . Chester died at 3 P.M. The other two are recovering rapidly." I have omitted the doctor's description of the unpleasant symptoms and the efforts of neighbors to administer antidotes or induce vomiting.

There are several varieties of *Cicuta* in the United States and Canada, in fact, one of them thrives as far north as Alaska, and England has its own lower-growing variety (*C. virosa*) and a closely related herb, *Oenanthe crocata*. Since water hemlock has killed scores of persons, especially children, in this country, it is hard to understand why the equally deadly *Conium* should have been introduced. Perhaps it was accidental; perhaps it was for the preparation of drugs, since the plant has been used from ancient times as a medicine. Whatever the reason, the poison hemlock now is also naturalized and spreads across most of the country in waste lands, as if not to usurp its native cousin's domain of moisture, on the edges of paths and lanes and near farm buildings. Its foliage, which is more lacy and curly, like parsley, makes it a more attractive plant than water hemlock.

Its record as a medicine predates Hippocrates, who listed it among the potent drugs, and Theophrastus had much to say about it. The best grade came from Susa and the best recipe for preparing it is described: "They first strip off the outside and take off the husk, since this is what causes the difficulty, as it is not easily assimilated; then they bruise it in a mortar, and, after putting it through a fine sieve, sprinkle it on water and so drink it; and then death is made swift and easy."

It was a potion similar to this which Socrates was sentenced to drink in 399 B.C., and in Plato's description of his death (in the following Benjamin Jowett translation) we have one of the first substantial accounts of the symptoms of a notorious poison:

> *Crito made a sign to the servant, who was standing by; and he went out, and having been absent for some time, returned with the jailer carrying the cup of poison. Socrates said: You, my good friend, who are experienced in these matters, shall give me directions how I am to proceed. The man answered: You have only to walk about until your legs are heavy, and then to lie down, and the poison will act. At the same time he handed the cup to Socrates, who in the easiest and gentlest manner, without the least fear of change of colour or feature, looking at the man with all his eyes, Echecrates, as his manner was, took the cup and said: What do you say about making a libation out of this cup to any god? May I, or not? The man answered: We only prepare, Socrates,*

*just so much as we deem enough. I understand, he said: but I may and must ask the gods to prosper my journey from this to the other world—even so—and so be it according to my prayer. Then raising the cup to his lips, quite readily and cheerfully he drank off the poison. And hitherto most of us had been able to control our sorrow; but now when we saw him drinking, and saw too that he had finished the draught, we could no longer forbear, and in spite of myself my own tears were flowing fast; so that I covered my face and wept, not for him, but at the thought of my own calamity in having to part from such a friend. Nor was I the first; for Crito, when he found himself unable to restrain his tears, had got up, and I followed; and at that moment, Apollodorus, who had been weeping all the time, broke out in a loud and passionate cry which made cowards of us all. Socrates alone retained his calmness: What is this strange outcry? he said. I sent away the women mainly in order that they might not misbehave in this way, for I have been told that a man should die in peace. Be quiet then, and have patience. When we heard his words we were ashamed, and refrained our tears; and he walked about until, as he said, his legs began to fail, and then he lay on his back, according to the directions, and the man who gave him the poison now and then looked at his feet and legs; and after a while he pressed his foot hard, and asked him if he could feel; and he said, No; and then his leg, and so upwards and upwards, and showed us that he was cold and stiff. And he felt them himself, and said: When the poison reaches the heart, that will be the end. He was beginning to grow cold about the groin, when he uncovered his face, for he had covered himself up, and said— they were his last words—he said: Crito, I owe a*

*cock to Asclepius; will you remember to pay the*
*debt? The debt shall be paid, said Crito; is there*
*anything else? There was no answer to this ques-*
*tion; but in a minute or two a movement was*
*heard, and the attendants uncovered him; his eyes*
*were set, and Crito closed his eyes and mouth.*

*Such was the end, Echecrates, of our friend;*
*concerning whom I may truly say, that of all the*
*men of his time whom I have known, he was the*
*wisest and justest and best.*

The ancient Hebrews knew hemlock as at least an
undesirable, bad plant. In Amos (6:12) we read, "For
ye have turned judgment into gall, and the fruit of right-
eousness into hemlock"; and in Hosea (10:4), "thus
judgment springeth up as hemlock in the furrows of the
field."

Naturally a plant of such power would be a simple
handed down from the Medeas and Circes of old to
medieval witches and physicians. In describing a witch,
Ben Jonson mentions "the stupefying hemlock," among
"the venom'd plants Wherewith she kills," and he includes
it in a witch's song about the herbs she has gathered.
Shakespeare's witches in *Macbeth* chant of "Root of hemlock digg'd i' the dark." And certainly all witches must
have known that the burning of a mixture of hemlock with
henbane, fennel, coriander and other herbs would summon
up a great host of demons. From more serious practi-
tioners of herbal lore, Galen, the Greek physician of the
second century, and Avicenna, the eleventh century
Arabian, we learn of a poultice of hemlock which would
subdue love's ardor—presumably applied to the heart?

But as always happens when a tradition continues too
long, there was a deterioration in knowledge derived from
inquiry into the potency of hemlock. *Bancke's Herbal*
(1525) told its readers: "The juice of this herb keepeth
maiden's teats small. Also, this herb oft drunken . . .

destroyeth the great appetite of lechery." Indeed the last statement, like defenestration as a cure for dandruff, must be right. William Coles' *Art of Simpling* contributes a tall tale of donkeys which, overcome by hemlock and presumed dead, were flayed for the leather, only to recover and awaken skinless, "to the griefe and amazement of the owners." A century later Culpeper was hardly more than suspicious; "very dangerous, especially to be taken inwardly," he wrote of *Conium*, but recommended the use of its leaves and root for external application in a variety of ailments. Of *Cicuta* varieties he said, "they are thought to be poisonous, but there is nothing certain on this head."

Though there was nothing "certain" for a few hundred years except the deaths of people who ate hemlock, in 1826 Giesecke isolated the alkaloid, coniine, from *Conium*. Still, that certainty did little to prevent the continuing fatalities due to ignorance and error. The instances go on concerning someone who thinks one or another of the hemlock roots is wild parsnip, ground artichoke, wild turnip or carrot—one man even mistook the leaves for parsley. Pammel, among other briefer citations, quotes a case, as reported in a newspaper, of a youth who found the roots lying exposed in a plowed field and ate some:

> *Virgil Hyatt, a high school boy, was poisoned last night while walking to the Ledges, a summer resort near Boone. He fell to the ground unconscious, and a companion carried him to a nearby farm house and summoned medical aid. . . . The trip was made in an automobile at record breaking speed. The boy was brought to a hospital here (Boone) but died just as he was being carried into the institution.*

One of the frequent problems in cases of hemlock poisoning is the difficulty of inducing the victim to vomit; the alkaloid has a sedative action, and it directly affects the motor centers and paralyzes, with the result that a condition like lockjaw prevents the administering of an emetic.

While these deadly hemlocks will probably not invade most gardens, the location of the garden might be a determining factor. A wild flower garden, especially beside a stream, or a garden around a country home could easily turn out to have a plant or two of *Cicuta* or *Conium* some fine spring day. Without even eating the leaves or roots, children have been poisoned by the plants. Since the stems are hollow, they appeal to the young as raw material for whistles or blow-pipes and the results are grim.

Through its long fascinating history, hemlock has been directed and pushed by men into some sort of useful category but at the moment their failure seems evident. Until fairly recently it was official in this country (it still is in the British Pharmacopoeia) but it has now been abandoned by medicine. This ignominy of the hemlock may be the curse of Socrates' outraged spirit.

# Henbane

## Hyoscyamus niger

*I*f ever a poisonous plant really looked poisonous, it is henbane. An annual or biennial herb, it has a long history of use as a medicine and a narcotic, and almost invariably those who have written of it have remarked upon its unpleasant odor. The lower leaves, broad, oblong and coarsely toothed, usually form a rosette lying on the ground and from it rises the main stem—three or four feet high—sometimes with almost no branching, but more often dividing into many branches with alternate leaves smaller than those in the basal rosettes. The gray-green leaves, like the stems and branches, are covered, especially along the veins, with long glandular hairs which secrete a sticky, clammy, fetid substance.

The flowers are like something conceived by Hieronymus Bosch. Funnel-shaped, they grow in spikes along the branching extremities from the axils where the leaves clasp around the stems. The corolla, along its outer edges, is scalloped into five lobes, and is of a lurid, sickly yellow-green hue. In its heart is a splotch of dark purple from which spreads all over the outer surface a repulsive network of purple veins. The blossoms look like a disease rendered visible. They rest in urn-shaped calyxes, which

in time hold an unusual seed capsule—it too is shaped
rather like an urn or a tobacco cannister and it has a top
just like a jar, which at maturity pops open to release the
many seeds inside.

This unpleasant herb, which is one of the nightshade
family, has been used in medicine from ancient times; its
generic name comes from the old Greek and means "hog's
bean"—it was thought that swine could eat the plant
without harm. How it came to be called henbane is not
clear. Some writers claim that it was *belene* in Anglo-
Saxon, which developed into "hen-bell"; others claim a
direct descent from the Anglo-Saxon *henn* plus *bana*
meaning "chicken-killer." In any case, since people
thought the seeds were fatal to chickens which ate them,
our common name springs at least from that notion.

Perhaps the earliest known medicinal use of the plant
was made by the Assyrians several millennia ago as a
remedy for toothache—still an efficient treatment today
and one continually recommended in the intervening centuries. Dioscorides and Celsus knew henbane as a pain-
killer and a soporific. Pliny, while noting that there are
several kinds and recommending them for treating toothache, gout, swellings, certain female troubles, and coughs,
warned that "all kinds cause insanity and giddiness." The
physician-poet, Nicander, in his comments on this herb,
included one of the major concerns of this book and
showed himself aware of one reason why children will eat
*anything:*

> *Let no one fill his belly, out of ignorance,*
> *With henbane, as men often do by fault or chance,*
> *Or children who, from swaddling-clothes, head-*
> *   bands and need*
> *To crawl unsurely on all fours but lately freed,*
> *And walking upright, with no anxious nurse*
> *   nearby,*

> *Through witlessness chew on the baleful flower-*
>   *spray,*
> *Since they are cutting incisor teeth along their*
>   *jaws*
> *Just then, which in their swollen gums sharp itch-*
>   *ings cause.*

Pliny, however, had more specific remarks about henbane: "A fourth kind is soft, downy, richer in juice than the others. . . . This is the kind that medical men have adopted. . . . It has the character of wine, and therefore injures the head and brain. Use is made of the seed as it is or when the juice has been extracted from it. The juice is extracted separately also from the stems and leaves. They also use the root, but the drug is, in my opinion, a dangerous medicine in any form."

Later physicians and herbalists added little to the knowledge of henbane or the uses to which it might be put until the present era, though all agreed that it is a dangerous plant. Gerard, Culpeper and others only elaborate on Dioscorides and Pliny. Meanwhile, the witches were not losing time. They used the plant to summon up evil spirits, and we recall it, along with hemlock and nightshade, in Ben Jonson's witch's song. The narcotic and hypnotic action of the drugs in henbane made it a plant of great importance in magic. Whether the witches brought the seeds to the United States with the Pilgrim Fathers or another group of settlers is not known, but henbane, a native of Central Europe and Asia, was recorded as growing in New England by 1672, and since then it has naturalized itself along a broad strip across the continent on both sides of the Canadian border.

Along with various animals whose hunger has driven them, in spite of their dislike of the herb, to eat the stinking leaves, henbane has killed or seriously poisoned many people. As few as twenty of the tiny seeds, like poppy-seeds in size, have taken the life of an adult. The young are more susceptible to the poisons and have died from eating even fewer seeds. In one account four children who had eaten some of the seeds lay unconscious in a death-like sleep for two entire days.

The poison, distributed throughout the plant, consists of several alkaloids—hyoscyamine, hyoscine and some atropine—and the effects are similar to those produced by atropine or belladonna. Hyoscine, better known as scopolamine, is even better known, in its combination with morphine, as the "twilight sleep" of painless and unremembered childbirth. It has also been known as "truth serum" and as such figured in one of the notable plays of 1945, *Home of the Brave* by Arthur Laurents. Hyoscine, as a poison agent, plays a minor part in Agatha Christie's story, "Philomel Cottage." In the true story of Dr. Hawley Harvey Crippen's murder of his plump wife, Cora, in 1910, however, it played a major role. The details are too fantastic and gruesome to try to condense here; you must read them for yourself.[1]

A man who experimented with henbane for himself was Gustav Schenk and he described the effects on him of fumes from the roasting seeds with his typical enthusiasm: "My limbs lost their certainty, pains hammered in my head, and I began to feel extremely giddy. . . . I had the feeling that my head had increased in size: it seemed to have grown broader, more solid, heavier. . . . My heart was beating loudly. I didn't hear it with my ears, for they seemed to be deaf. . . . The room dances; the floor, the walls and the ceiling tilt slowly to the right and then back to the left. . . . Everything suddenly amused me. . . . I was seized by a raging impulse to move. Since my feet seemed firmly welded to the floor, I could only clutch and grasp

[1] Thorwald, *The Century of the Detective,* pp. 175–187; Edmund Pearson, *Murder at Smutty Nose,* Dolphin Books, (New York, Doubleday & Company, Inc.), pp. 117–125.

at things with my hands and tear them to pieces. . . . There were animals, which looked at me keenly with contorted grimaces and staring, terrified eyes; there were flying stones and clouds of mist. . . . I was flung into a flaring drunkenness, a witches' caldron of madness. Above my head was flowing, dark and blood-red. . . . Every part of my body seemed to be going off on its own. My head was growing independently larger, and I was seized with the fear that I was falling apart." And so on.[2]

The introduction of the chemicals in henbane into the body by means of fumes is an old therapeutic practice, dating back at least as far as Pliny. In modern medicine it is the extracted alkaloids which are most frequently used, though inhaling the fumes of the plant is sometimes recommended by homeopaths. Scopolamine (hyoscine), because of its sedative action which affects the brain and results in wiping out the memory, is an important drug in the treatment of mental patients. For those same reasons, it has been used since the first World War in brain-washing, though in recent years, during the Korean War and since, it seems to have been replaced by LSD, a drug derived from ergot, a fungous growth found on grain and grasses.

What strange contrary qualities henbane has! It is a valuable source of medicines, so much so that in many countries it is grown as a botanical drug crop, and modern research into its potentials continues. And yet this repulsive plant seems to try to reflect its appearance in its choice of habitats—waste places, rubbish piles, garbage dumps and dung heaps.

[2] Schenk, *The Book of Poisons*, pp. 43–49.

# Jimsonweed

## Datura stramonium

*W*hen the early colonists landed on the shores of Virginia and established a settlement at Jamestown, one of their problems was to find a source of food. A possible answer, at least in part, appeared to be the large, smooth green leaves of an unknown plant almost as tall as a man, which they found growing there. Though these leaves, about eight inches long, with wavy-toothed edges, had a rather rank odor, the long purple or white trumpets of the angular blossoms had a sweet smell. Without benefit of counsel from the native Indians, they cooked up messes of the spinach-like leaves as pot herbs and ate them, "the Effect of which," wrote the historian, Robert Beverly, "was a very pleasant Comedy; for they turn'd natural Fools upon it for several Days. One would blow a Feather in the Air; another would dart Straws at it with much Fury; and another stark naked was sitting up in a Corner, like a Monkey grinning and making Mows at them; a Fourth would fondly kiss and paw his Companions, and snear in their Faces, with a Countenance more antik than any in a Dutch Doll. In this frantik Condition they were confined, lest they in their Folly should destroy themselves; though it was observed that all their Actions were full of Innocence and Good Nature. Indeed, they were not very cleanly; for they would have wallow'd in their own Excrements, if they had not been prevented. A Thousand such simple Tricks they play'd, and after Eleven Days, return'd themselves again, not remembering anything that had pass'd."

After that, the colonists had other, not quite so comic, experiences with the plant and tried, unsuccessfully, to exterminate it. It was given the name of Jamestown weed and in a short time, by the processes of diminution and corruption, the name became "Jimson-weed."

This plant, a member of the nightshade family, is also known as thorn apple because the fruit is a green capsule about the size of a walnut and covered with prickles. It is an annual, native in North America and the tropics, though other species are perennial and, in fact, in South America can grow into small trees up to fifteen feet high. The generic name, *Datura*, is from Hindu. The plant may have been confused by the older Greeks and Romans with its kinsmen, the nightshades. One cannot tell which *strychnos* of the various ones discussed may be *Datura*. But Dioscorides wrote specifically of it: "The root being drank with wine the quantity of a drachma hath the power to effect not unpleasant fantasies. But two drachmas being drank make one beside himself for three days; and four being drank, kill him." It is thought that the plant, *hippomanes*, in Theocritus' "Idyll II" is *Datura*:

> *This herb, colt's-madness, with wild juices fills*
> *stallions and mares that stamp Arcadian hills.*[1]

In Asia and South America where several species of *Datura* thrive, its medicinal and narcotic uses have long been known. It was a remedy for rheumatic ailments in

[1] *Theocritus, The Complete Poems*, trans. by Jack Lindsay (Fanfrolico Press, 1930).

China and India, for asthma and influenza (by inhaling the fumes) among the Arabians in Africa and, again smoked, a substitute for opium among the Turks—who are not alone in liking to conjure up "not unpleasant fantasies." In Mexico an infusion of the leaves has been used for intoxication and, as it is used by the Indians in South America, for making a person receptive to the revelations of the spirits, much as the Oracles at Delphi used it, or whatever they did use. In India, mothers have dripped the juice of thorn apple onto their nipples in order to do away with inconvenient female babies. The ancient Chibcha Indian tribe in Colombia used it to narcotize wives and slaves before burying them alive with their dead husbands and masters.

Gerard, in his time, apparently knew no uses for the plant except as a healer of wounds and burns and as an anodyne. His prescriptions for burns and wounds are these:

> *The juice of Thorn-apples boiled with hogs grease to the form of an unguent or salve, cures all inflammations whatsoever, all manner of burnings or scaldings, as well of fire, water, boiling lead, gun pouder, as that which comes by lightning.*
>
> *The leaves stamped small and boiled with oile Olive untill the herbs be as it were burnt, then strained and set to the fire again, with some wax, rosin, and a little turpentine, and made into a salve, doth most speedily cure new and fresh wounds.*

Gerard introduced the *Datura* into England, having got the seeds of *D. metel*, as he says, from *"John Robin of Paris, an excellent Herbarist,"* and seeds of another species, probably *D. stramonium*, from "the right honourable the Lord *Edward Zouch*; which he brought from Constantinople, and of his liberalitie did bestow them upon me. . . . and it is that Thorn-apple that I have dispersed through this land, whereof at this present I have great use in Surgery." He seems to have "dispersed" well, for the plant grows wild, quite at home, in many localities of England. His reference to its use in surgery is, of course, related to the narcotic properties in the alkaloids, as it was one of the several plants which could be used in operations to deaden pain or put the patient into a deep sleep before modern anaesthetics were discovered.

However, the jimsonweed's narcotic powers were often put to less honorable uses. Witches used it to good effect in their rites of incantation and who knows for what other purposes? Schenk relates several instances of sinister uses of *Datura*,[2] one of which concerns Goa during the time of the Portuguese Indian Empire: "The plant is said to be misused by two kinds of dishonest people, namely by lewd women and thieves," who intend to rob their stupefied or comatose victims—a method also followed by faithless servants who planned to rob their masters. Thorn apple's drugs were employed in England for the same purposes by thieves who found their victims in taverns.

*Datura*, the thorn apple, contains a complex of alkaloids which is very similar to those of belladonna—principally hyoscyamine, along with stropine and scopolamine. Thus, the drugs have a narcotic, mydriatic, antispasmodic and anodyne effect when properly administered; when taken to excess, they cause dry throat, great thirst, vertigo, impaired sight, lack of muscular control, convulsions, and death. As Kingsbury put it: "Symptoms are spectacular. . . . Subjects may become . . . incoherent in speech and apparently insane. They commonly pick at imaginary objects on themselves or in the air. In severe cases the subjects usually experience convulsions and coma."[3]

Though grazing animals have frequently suffered,

[2] Schenk, *The Book of Poisons*, pp. 39–42.

[3] Kingsbury, *Deadly Harvest*, p. 79.

the greater number of victims seems to be children, whose misfortunes with jimsonweed have been recorded down the years. One of the more innocent ways in which they have been poisoned has been the sucking of the nectar from the flowers; Pammel cites several such cases. John W. Harshberger reprinted an account of *Datura* poisoning from the Philadelphia *Ledger* of October 12, 1909:

> *A verdict of death by accidental poisoning by eating seeds of stramonium, or jimson-weed plant was found by a coroner's jury yesterday in the case of Martha Robinson, 3 years old. . . . Martha and her little friend, Helen Bradley, attracted by the curiously shaped seed pods of the weed . . . had broken several of them open and had eaten the seeds. Both children became sick and went home where antidotes were administered to them, but failed to overcome the toxic effects in the case of Martha Robinson, who died in agony. Helen Bradley was apparently on the road to recovery yesterday.*

A more recent case, reported in the *New England Journal of Medicine* (August 30, 1962), involved a three-year-old-boy and his six-year-old-sister who ate the seeds of jimsonweed. Within three hours the boy "became markedly confused and disoriented and displayed muscular inco-ordination," fell asleep for two hours, then had a convulsion and was hospitalized as a possible sufferer from encephalitis. A few hours later his sister was admitted to the hospital; she was hyperactive and "her behavior suggested visual and auditory hallucinations." Fortunately, some playmates had seen them eat the seeds and proper treatment could be applied to effect their recovery.

One of the most curious cases of such poisoning was produced by the eating of tomatoes grown on a plant grafted to jimsonweed; both are of course nightshades. It had seemed a good idea to effect the graft in order to make the tomato resistant to frost and thus bear fruit in the early winter. The two men in Tennessee who did so knew nothing of the family relationship or of the toxic nature of jimsonweed. Five persons were poisoned by a single tomato from one of the grafts and two of them required hospital treatment. The graft made by the other man did not poison anyone; he had removed all jimsonweed leaves from the stock, but the man whose family was poisoned had let these leaves grow below the tomato graft. As evidence of the high incidence of poisoning of children by jimsonweed, authorities cited in the *New Yorker* article which recounts the tomato graft story point out:[4]

> *During the past five years at the University of Virginia Hospital, which services a large southern rural area,* Datura *has accounted for approximately four per cent of pediatric patients admitted because of ingestion of a toxic substance. . . .* Datura *has had about the same incidence as lead, barbiturates, alcohol, rodenticides, and insecticides as a source of poisoning.*

While it is clearly not a plant to trifle with or to nibble at, it is a most valuable drug plant. What has already been said of the potentialities for good in deadly nightshade and henbane can apply as well to jimsonweed, for similar alkaloids are present in all three. Because of its antispasmodic action, it is still, after thousands of years of like prescription, recommended for asthma. There are many other beneficial uses for the drug, but modern research into the plant, now actively going forward, may provide new and dramatic applications for it.

Jimsonweed may, at some unknown time, have had a day as an ornamental, but that day is past, and it is valued, *when* valued, as a drug plant. In its naturalized

[4] *The New Yorker*, May 15, 1965, in "Annals of Medicine" by Berton Roueché, pp. 180 ff.

state it grows on the edges of rich fields, in waste lands and vacant lots, along roadsides and railroad yards and, oddly, on burnt-over land—a choice habitat which has given it another common name, fireweed. But there are other *Daturas* which are grown in gardens and are not considered weeds. A favorite (*D. metel* or *fastuosa*), a native of India but naturalized in the American semi-tropical regions, has a purple calyx around a corolla which is white inside and pale yellow or violet outside. A native Western species (*D. meteloides*) is a handsome perennial with sweet, rose-tinged white flowers, which might well be found in a garden; in earlier times this plant was used by some Indian tribes in puberty rites as well as in medicine. In gardens in Florida and California can be found the perennial angel trumpet (*D. arborea*), a small tree from the Andes of Peru which produces very large white flowers. All of these more attractive garden specimens are equally poisonous, or more so, than the common jimson-weed.

# Manchineel

## Hippomane mancinella

$T$his small tree is, you may well be thankful to know, the least likely of any of the plants I have treated to turn up in your garden, unless it is situated on the seacoast of southern Florida. It is difficult to accept Samuel Eliot Morison's statement in *The Caribbean As Columbus Saw It* that "the tree itself is sufficiently safe to be used as an ornamental plant" in the West Indies. Certainly it is in no sense "safe," and, though I have only been to a few of the Caribbean islands, I have never seen it cultivated. Perhaps, with good reason, it is grown in botanical gardens.

The West Indies and the shores of the lower Caribbean Sea and the Gulf of Mexico are its habitat. Its appearance in lower Florida may have resulted from high tides or hurricane seas which floated the "apples" over the intervening water to establish colonies on this continent. Whether it prefers the seashores and watery locations or grows along the coastlines by accidental implantation of its seeds is, I suppose, open to investigation. However, since it now grows in Florida, it might not be amiss to assume that the Everglades are infested with the tree.

Manchineel is an English corruption of *manzanillo,*

Spanish for "little apple tree"; the fruit, a drupe, looks somewhat like a crab apple. These yellowish "apples" are produced from small, greenish flowers which blossom along a stiff spike emerging from terminal clusters of leaves. The flowers are of separate sexes, with a few females at the base of the spike and clusters of males higher up. The leaves are not unattractive; springing from long petioles, they have a pointed, broad, elliptical shape and a fine sheen.

As a member of the spurge family, the manchineel secretes under its smooth, pale brown bark an extremely caustic, milky sap. The toxic element in the sap is also present in the leaves and fruit. American Indians of the Antilles used to poison arrows with the juice. When Christopher Columbus made his second voyage to the new world, he anchored, in November of 1498, off the island of Marie-Galante and found it growing there.

Many another early explorer and settler made the same error in assuming the apples to be edible. One can easily imagine the irritating juices so inflaming and swelling the throat that the consumer of the fruit would die of suffocation before he died of any direct action of the poison on his digestive tract.

Shortly after the turn of the century a British doctor, Sir Frederick Treves, made a voyage around the ports and islands of the Caribbean. In his account of his travels, *The Cradle of the Deep* (1908), he describes the manchineel on Barbados:

> *Certain of the curving bays are shaded by thickets of trees which crowd to the very margin of the shore. Some are inviting, modest-looking trees, which call to mind the orchard trees in England. They bear, moreover, a small green fruit, an apple, which might tempt a thirsty man. Woe to him if he yields, if even the temptress be Eve! For these*

> *are the manchineel, the poison trees; the shade*
> *they offer is tainted; their leaves will blister the*
> *skin; the fruit will turn to worse than ashes in the*
> *mouth; their innocence is feigned, for the orchard*
> *by the sea is an upas grove, shunned by every*
> *living thing except the land crab.*
>
> *Nelson, in his early days, was made very ill*
> *by drinking from a pool into which some branches*
> *of manchineel had been thrown. In the opinion of*
> *some his health 'received thereby a severe and*
> *lasting injury.'*

In spite of his hyperbole, Sir Frederick had, at least in this instance, witnessed what he wrote of (as was not always his habit) for he took a photograph of the grove. From my own observations, I should say the manchineel was not nearly as noxious as the upas tree, nor "shunned by every living thing." On Montserrat I drove over a figment of a road to a charming little bay with a black sand beach lined with handsome specimens of manchineel. About a dozen warning signs, stating that the trees were poisonous and the fruit on the ground should not be touched, were nailed to as many trunks. At that time of the year the ground was scattered with the remains of last autumn's apples. But a road, wretched though it was, led there and on the evidence of the litter of charred wood, cartons, beer cans, bottles, and other refuse of picnickers, the spot was anything but shunned. Obviously the visitors took care to heed the warning signs.

On many of the islands, especially where the trees grow along choice beaches, the authorities are trying to exterminate the manchineel. To a great extent this has been accomplished on the Florida shores, where the growth was a serious vexation to the early settlers. But even in destroying the trees, the men sometimes suffered severely from them, for the heavy bite of an ax into the bark could send the virulent sap squirting into the chopper's eyes. People, writes Kingsbury, "were temporarily and sometimes permanently blinded." It is also dangerous to burn the wood, because the smoke can carry the irritant substance to the nose and eyes of anyone in its path.

# Mandrake and Mayapple

## Mandragora officinarum and

## Podophyllum peltatum

*U*ndoubtedly the top of the top ten poisonous plants, in view of its colorful history, is the mandrake. It is a European plant of the nightshade family and seems not to have been introduced into this country or at least not to have survived the winters, and thus is most unlikely to appear in your garden. However, there is a native American plant frequently called mandrake which might well come to live in a moist woodland garden. The English also have a makeshift for mandrake called bryony. But let us consider the true mandrake—*mandragora*—first, and begin with the Biblical story of the birth of Joseph.

From Genesis: "And Reuben went in the days of wheat harvest, and found mandrakes in the field, and brought them unto his mother Leah. Then Rachel said to Leah, Give me, I pray thee, of thy son's mandrakes. . . . And God remembered Rachel. . . . And she conceived, and bare a son." So, in most ancient times, the virtues of the plant in aiding barren women were established and it is a virtue which has not been thoroughly discredited to this day. In her recent fascinating book, *Green Medicine,* Margaret Kreig reports on investigations of Indian plants conducted in Bombay: " 'Sterile' women given an extract from poisonous mandrake, which has a 'man-shaped root' like ginseng, have consistently given birth to boy babies."

In the centuries dividing these two citations, mandrake, without losing its reputation as a remedy for barren women, acquired, by natural association of cause and effect, the properties of a love philtre. The fact that it produced a narcotic and hallucinatory sensation helped, of course, in working its magic. It was called the Herb of Circe, who was certainly instructed in its use by her superior, Hecate, and it may well have been the drug she put into the wine of Ulysses' mates to turn them into swine.

The Greeks used it as an anaesthetic—it was known to Hippocrates—and in Roman times Pliny recommended that the root be chewed as a pain-killer by a patient about to undergo a painful operation. Theophrastus had prescribed the root as good for "erysipelas, when scraped and steeped in vinegar, and also for gout, for sleeplessness, and for love potions." The plant was so closely associated with love potions, in fact, that Aphrodite was sometimes given the epithet Mandragoris.

Even in his day Theophrastus seemed skeptical about the traditional ceremonies of gathering such magic plants as mandragora. "Thus," he writes, "it is said that one should draw three circles round mandrake with a sword, and cut it with one's face towards the west; and at the cutting of the second piece one should dance round the plant and say as many things as possible about the mysteries of love." As time went on and magical ideas flourished, the rites for digging up mandrake roots proliferated. Pliny had clarified Theophrastus only to the point of saying that the digger should stand, not merely to westward, but to windward, because of the obnoxious odor.

Much later, in the medieval age, with the development of the notion that the plant grew from a human figure—the thick roots were often found divided into two carrot-like tubers, like human legs—the legend spread that the plant below the soil was a humanoid organism, generated below the gallows by the semen spilled by hanged men and that the organism shrieked when pulled from the ground. Anyone who dug it up would die or go mad at the sound of its cries, and therefore complicated methods of forcing dogs to uproot the plant were worked out, though few rational writers of the period gave any more credit to the superstitions than by simply recording them.

Curiously, similar superstitions attached to the gathering of other herbs. Theophrastus comments on the ceremonies required in digging hellebore, wild rose, honeysuckle, peony, *thapsia*, feverwort and iris by saying that they "in some cases may be to the point" (that is, to stay to windward in case of spurting juices, as for instance from the manchineel), "but in others contain exaggeration."

Even more remote and astonishing, the Chinese have attached a legend to the ginseng (an aromatic root somewhat like ginger); according to Sir Edwin Arnold, when it is pulled "from the earth it is thought to utter a low musical cry." In addition to the coincidence of the anthropomorphic superstition, it is surprising to realize that the names of the two herbs are similarly constructed: mandrake is "man" plus "drake" or dragon (Old English from the Latin *draco*) and ginseng is a compound of Mandarin "jên," meaning "man," and "shên," whose meaning is obscure. The physique of man, suggested in the shape of the roots, has given the plants the first syllable of their names and has inspired the legend of their outraged cries when uprooted. The superstition went so far that fifteenth century herbals include engravings or woodcuts of mandrake as leaves and flowers sprouting from the heads of male and female human figures.

Mandragora became something of a panacea. For cauterization and operations Dioscorides had said it could make a man "sensible of nothing for three or four hours." It was an aphrodisiac, indeed a necessary one to incite elephants to copulation, it could soften ivory to the consistency of putty, could cure "devil sickness or insanity," barrenness in women and—the application I like best, given by Pseudo-Apuleius—"if one see some heavy mischief in his home." A suggestion to murder?

What with all this background of legend, superstition, and actual drugging properties, it was a natural for poets and other witches down the centuries. One of Ben Jonson's witches is treated to these words:

> *The venom'd plants*
> *Wherewith she kills! where the sad mandrake*
>     *grows,*
> *Whose groans are deathful; the dead-numbing*
>     *night-shade,*
> *The stupefying hemlock, adder's tongue,*
> *And martagan.*

Shakespeare's Cleopatra orders Charmian:

> *. . . give me to drinke* Mandragora.
> *Charmian: Why Madam?*
> *Cleopatra: That I might sleepe out this great gap*
>     *of time:*
>     *My* Anthony *is away.*

And Juliet, thinking on her feigned death by Friar Lawrence's potion and her fear that the drug might wear off too soon in the sepulchre, cried:

> *Alacke, alacke, is it not like that I*
> *So early waking, what with loathsome smels,*

> *And shrikes like Mandrakes torne out of the earth,*
> *That living mortals hearing them, run mad.*

Almost too well known even to need re-quoting, after naming the poet, is John Donne's line, "Get with child a Mandrake root." Then there is Machiavelli's comedy, *Mandragola*, which Stark Young translated many years ago.

In this play a rich old man, Nicia, is worried about his sterile wife, and a young lusty mountebank, Callimaco, proposes the remedy:

> *You must hear that there's nothing more certain to bring on conception than a potion made of mandragola. It's a thing I've experimented with twice a couple of times and always found it true; if it were not so the queen of France would be sterile and countless other princesses of that realm.*

When Nicia agrees to give his wife the potion, Callimaco warns:

> *Now you must think of this point; the man that first lies with her after she has taken this potion, dies in eight days; nothing in the world could save him.*
> *Nicia: O pox, I don't want such a torment as that on my hands.*
> *Callimaco: Be easy, there's a remedy. . . . Make another sleep with her right off, so that he will draw to himself by passing the night with her all the infection of the mandragola; after that you can lie with her without danger.*
> *Nicia: I don't want to do this.*
> *Callimaco: Why?*
> *Nicia: Because I don't want to make my wife a whore and me a cuckold.*
> *Callimaco: What are you saying? . . . Do you*

*hesitate to do what the king of France has done and so many noble gentlemen of his?*

Thus, in the above brief anthology we can see reflected the lethal, narcotic and aphrodisiac properties of mandrake, along with a certain amused cynicism about its legend of curing sterility.

The narcotic application of mandrake was carried even further. Until the thirteenth century it was one of few pain-killing drugs, one which could be used to comatize a person during an operation or an amputation. Then came one of the first complicated anaesthesias, the "soporific sponge," which was steeped in mandrake, along with opium, hemlock, henbane and other less deadly herbs, and when needed, moistened and given the patient to inhale before his flesh was cut into. Its use continued almost to the seventeenth century.

The magical properties of an herb such as mandrake were bound to be multiplied—though enervated in the process. Observing this, Gerard, who in spite of lapses was a no-nonsense man, had spoken out: "There hath beene many ridiculous tales brought up of this plant, whether of old wives, or some runnagate Surgeons or Physicke-mongers I know not. . . . Besides many fables of loving matters, too full of scurrilitie to set forth in print, which I forbeare to speake of. All which dreames and old wives tales you shall from henceforth cast out of your bookes and memory; knowing this, that they are all and everie part of them false and most untrue." He even discounted the Biblical story of Jacob and Leah. But as he could probably foresee, his rational approach was doomed.

The roots became treasured as amulets and charlatans began to manufacture them of the thick roots of bryony, the English "mandrake." These fakers would carve the tubers to improve the physical resemblances, implant seeds of millet or barley in tiny pricked holes in the roots, bury them in sand till the rootlets sprouted, and after trimming the hairs to their fancy sell the "mandrake" at good prices. The business of imitation reached such profitable heights that molds were fashioned to be fitted around the still growing roots to force them into the desired forked human shape.

In England there are several types of bryony; the plant does not grow in the United States. The white bryonies (so-called for their yellow-white tubers) are members of the cucumber family, and climb through shrubs and up trees by means of tendrils. The flowers are small and greenish and, like those of Indian hemp, are unisexual, the male on one plant, the female on another. The scarlet or black pea-sized berries, which hang in scanty clusters, contain a fetid juice. The carrot-like roots, growing to huge size—"of the bignes of a child of a yeare old," Gerard reported of one he had seen—have been a popular source of cathartic and purgative medicine from the Greeks to the present-day homeopaths, though their violent nature makes them dangerous. To the French the plant is known as "devil's turnip" (*navet du diable*). As to the special properties of bryony, Theophrastus at least was more restrained in prescribing it than latter-day medicinemen; the root, he said, is "heating and pungent: wherefore it is useful as a depilatory and to remove freckles: and the fruit is useful for smoothing hides."

The black bryony is of another family, which includes the yam, and it of course has a root which is black on the outside and which is, though recommended for treating many ailments, very poisonous. "Death in most painful form is the result of an overdose," write Grieve and Leyel in *A Modern Herbal*. Its name simply confuses the nomenclature of bryony, not that of mandrake, for apparently only the true red-berried bryony is called mandrake in England.

The plant called mandrake in the United States, the

one which could take up residence in some sorts of gardens, probably has more positive virtues than those mentioned above. It is, at any rate, far more amiable in all respects. More generally called Mayapple than mandrake or its botanical name, *Podophyllum peltatum*, it is a member of the barberry family and an extremely tidy plant. From a thick rhizome the smooth stem shoots up and puts forth two large leaves, between whose Y-fork a single flower emerges. Sometimes only one leaf is produced, attached at its center to the stem—a vegetable umbrella—in which case, since there is no fork between the leaf-stalks, no flower appears.

Mayapple loves damp open woods and pastures, which it finds throughout the eastern half of this country. It grows from a foot to a foot and a half high, with circular but deeply lobed leaves, sometimes twelve inches across, stretching horizontally above the ground, drooping slightly at the edges, and the plants spread across rich soil in big, densely populated patches. To come upon one of these large colonies in a wood or a forgotten moist meadow, to stand a short distance from the border of the colony, is a delightful, exhilarating experience, faintly awesome indeed. For what you are looking at is, inexplicably, a sort of verdant shining carpet suspended a foot or more above the floor of the wilderness. At the edges, true, you can see a line of supporting stems but above and stretching away, the broad leaves overlap, crowd together and intertwine to make a fairly even, floating, wavering expanse, patterned with highlights from the sun and dark arabesques where the leaf-tips, bending down or failing to touch, let the shadow below show through.

And in that shade beneath the great green floating carpet, the simple white flowers open on short drooping stems, mature and form yellow, lemon-shaped "apples." Except for the pulp of these fruits, the other parts of the plant—leaves, seeds and especially roots—are poisonous. But for years the ripe fruit has been used as a food. In its raw fresh state because, as one writer put it, it tastes "mawkish, eaten by pigs and boys," it is not much used unless its juice is added as a flavoring to fruit drinks or alcoholic punches. It is highly recommended, however, as a basic ingredient for making marmalade or jelly—Gibbons gives a recipe for marmalade of a delicious flavor which he cannot quite describe.

The plant was discovered in this country by early settlers and explorers and they learned not only of the edible property of the fruit but the medicinal property of the root. This knowledge they got from the Indians. William Bartram, in 1789, answered in detail a group of questions put to him by the American Ethnological Society with these words on diseases and remedies of the Indians of the southern regions. This quotation is only an excerpt from his much broader discussion:

> *Through the emollient and discutient power of the Hypo or May apple* (Podophyllum peltatum)—*the root of which is the most effectual and safe emetic, and also cathartic and equally efficacious in expelling worms from the stomach—the lives of many thousands of people of the southern States are preserved, both of children and adults.*

Mayapple, especially in the fleshy acrid roots, contains podophyllin and acts not only as a violent drug affecting the liver and the gastro-intestinal tract, but also upon all other parts of the body. In infusions, dedoctions and tinctures it has been prescribed for dropsy, dyspepsia, biliousness, complaints of the liver, skin diseases and other ailments. But while there are many plant drugs which are effective cathartics and purgatives, Mayapple has one special power in its poison which not too many other plants have, and one only discovered in recent years. One of the compounds in the plant's resinoid was found to have "selective ability to kill certain types of cells and has been put to use in treating some kinds of undesired growths on the human body," wrote Kingsbury.

The remedies of magic, witch medicines, and herbs have been applied to so many ailments that it would seem only probable that some of the applications might be beneficial. Margaret Kreig, pointing out that in this age of miracle drugs, open-minded scientists are paying more attention to and investigating the claims of the ancient herbalists, cites the case of Dr. Jonathan Hartwell, who examined the "quack cure" of the Penobscot Indians for cancer, which was an herb. "Today," she wrote, "an extract of this plant, podophyllin, from American mandrake or May apple, *Podophyllum peltatum*, is the preferred treatment for certain warts, and some cancer specialists use it for other skin growths." In Switzerland, she goes on to say, an anti-cancer agent has been derived from *Podophyllum* which in many cases "inhibited the growth of certain solid, malignant tumors and, in most favorable cases, led to a clinical disappearance of the tumors during the period of observation. The best results have been obtained in tumors of the upper digestive tract and in breast cancer that has spread to the lungs."

Under whatever name, in whatever family, what an ambiguous mandrake! It has, indeed, as Edmund Spenser wrote, "The powre of herbes, both which can hurt and ease." The "ease" results when a physician administers the proper dosages of the herb's toxin. As to the "hurt," just remember that the Arabs call the mandrake "the devil's testicles."

# *Mushrooms*

### *Agaricaceae species*

*A*lthough no one is going to plant mushrooms in a garden, these fungi do spring up in the most unexpected places. Some people, however, do grow mushrooms as a private source of food or a commercial venture. One of my friends some years ago responded to one of those ads for getting rich (which she didn't need to do), and planted the spawn in her basement and sold the crop to a local market. Delicious it was, too. But think, on the other hand, of what happened in a similar situation in Ray Bradbury's story, "Come Into My Cellar" in which a child orders the spawn from an ad and grows it—not death by poisoning but something worse.

The aforesaid suggests the great trouble with mushrooms: they are either a most delectable dish or they are a most deadly poison and it is tricky for an amateur who wishes to make a gourmet meal from them to tell which is which. This is a situation in which parents must be warned not so much to protect their little ones from eating some poisonous plant, but to protect themselves against the demon of mycophilia (love of mushrooms). Oddly enough, children, I think, are less likely than grown-ups to eat the mushrooms they find. Perhaps it is conditioning

*(200)*

*Amanita bisporigera*

by their juvenile reading, an association of "toadstools," or simply that the pallid white look of most mushrooms and their strange texture makes them less appealing than bright green leaves, red berries or vari-colored flowers.

All writers on the subject issue dire warnings to the novice, which can be summed up thus: "The odds in this hobby are neavily against the collector." Fernald and Kinsey point out that many safe and toxic types are so similar that only an expert can distinguish between them and state that the beginner "should never allow himself to be tempted into eating any mushroom unless he is absolutely certain of its identity." Though there are hundreds of edible species, writes Gibbons, the Indians rarely ate them, maybe out of the wisdom of incertitude. He notes as well that there are no short-cut tests, such as silver spoons, bites of field-mice, etc., and he predicts that the uninstructed amateur "is likely to poison himself." In the best, and most reasonably priced, book I know on the subject, Alexander H. Smith gives six precautionary rules; Fernald and Kinsey list eight instructions for gathering wild mushrooms. The many warnings cannot be gone into here, since it would take a booklet to explain them adequately. Just don't eat the mushrooms that pop up suddenly in your garden unless you know definitely that they are edible.

For the plant can appear at any place the wind can carry its minute spores, provided they fall upon soil or a log suitable for their germination. The mushroom is a fascinating plant, but not so strange as Theophrastus thought it. To him it lacked most of the parts of a plant—leaves, branches, flowers, roots. He did not realize that he had never truly considered the *plant*, which lies underground, but was only observing the flower, or fruit (just as it is the flowers of broccoli and cauliflower which we eat). By the time of Culpeper, people knew somewhat more: the plant grew from "a white mouldy substance called spawn, which produces numerous white knots or embryo plants, gradually increasing in size to the perfect mushroom." Culpeper considered them fit not for food but for poultices; however, it is said that Anglo-Saxons have never cared greatly for this delicious vegetable.

When the spores of the fungus fall to earth they begin to grow. If the situation is wrong, they soon die; if it is right, they flourish. The plant—the spawn (*mycelium*)—is a mass of minute threads, like mold, which grow under soil or humus, or through the crevices of decaying wood.

The visible mushroom, the flower, matures into the fruit, bearing the spores to be wafted away by the wind to form another generation.

Certain species are very particular. In general, however, they all divide between terrestrial—those living in the humus of the forest—or lignicolous—those which live on wood which is buried under soil. The terrestrial plant can live on and on, since each year the deposit of autumn leaves and dead plants adds to its food supply. But the spawn of the wood-living types dies when it has consumed all the food in the piece of wood upon which it feeds. The spores of each type have, nevertheless, spread the plant elsewhere.

To explain further: the mushrooms, called "nature's destroyers," cannot function as other plants do, which use chlorophyll (the cause of the green color of most vegetation) and sunlight to manufacture food out of inorganic matter such as water and the minerals in soil and convert it into organic matter. Mushrooms contain no chlorophyll, therefore are never green, and can feed only by destroying ready-made, one might say, "instant," foodstuffs. They digest the dead vegetation on the forest floor or the lignin and cellulose of wood. Thus, the terrestrial types have a new supply of food each season while the lignicolous types have nothing more than the immediate chunks of wood they are consuming.

Mushrooms are even more fastidious in their choices of homes. Some will grow only on conifers; some only on hardwood; some only under poplars, maples, beeches, firs, pines, etc. They take all sorts of shapes from the familiar "toadstool" to puffballs, sponges, coral and hanging forms, shaggy and fleecy like waterfalls. And they are not only white, but can be red, yellow, orange, brown or spotted. As to edibility, they range from the most delicious golden-apricot chanterelles and tawny morels to the deadly *Amanitas*, one of which because of its day-long delayed symptoms, always kills, charting up more deaths than bites of rattlesnakes. John Collier has given us a grimly amusing story, "Three Bears Cottage," in which a mushroom-loving man and wife each decides to eliminate the other with a dish of *Amanita phalloides* and both succeed at the same time.

In the realm of truth—as recorded by history, that is—one of the most famous poisonings by mushrooms was that of the Emperor Claudius by his wife, Agrippina. Tacitus records it and Juvenal alludes to it in his fifth satire:

> *Suspicious toadstools will be served to the lowly guests;*
> *To the master, a mushroom such as Claudius ate before*
> *That one his wife prepared, after which he ate nothing more.*

One of the fairly limited connections of the mushroom with magic and the supernatural is the "fairy ring," which appears overnight in rich green grass and is indeed a perfect circle of small mushrooms. Being terrestrial the underground plants can live for years, ever expanding as the spawn of the *Agaricus arvensis* reaches outward in all directions. The legend is that the rings were caused by the feet of fairies dancing a round on the grass at night. Some rings are so large that they scarcely resemble circles any longer and are estimated to be scores of years old.

The greater part of all these fungi is water, but they do contain much nutritious mineral matter, including a major component of vitamin D, as well as sulphur and calcium. In its way it is the vegetable kingdom's best substitute for meat. Some of its kin have, in recent years, been discovered to contain possibly useful medicines, though just how to use them—for mental conditions—has not yet been determined.

These varieties are in the genus *Panaeolus*, specifically *Psilocyle mexicana*, the "sacred mushroom" or *teonanacatl* ("God's flesh") of the Aztecs. A historian of these ancient inhabitants of Mexico, Tezozomoc, recorded that it was part of the feast for the coronation of Montezuma in 1502. Catholic priests complained that the mushrooms "are harmful and intoxicate like wine." In spite of other such "leaks" of information, it was only in the thirties that the plant was discovered by non-Mexicans and another two decades passed before the well-hidden secret plant was seen by an outsider. This investigator eventually witnessed the sacred rite of the mushroom ceremony which, still observed today, is a mixture of pagan and Christian elements. The property of this particular fungus as a hallucinogen, like peyote and "devil's morning glory," is what spurs further investigation into its medicinal potentials.

Curiously, in this connection, Oliver Goldsmith in 1762 had recounted the story of Siberian peasants who got drunk on a brew made from poisonous mushrooms. Some scholars have speculated on whether Dr. Charles L. Dodgson was not aware of this report and of the hallucinogenic effects of certain fungi and slyly alluded to it in *Alice in Wonderland*. When Alice meets the Caterpillar, she is only three inches high and distressed about her size. The Caterpillar, rather bored with her complaints, departs with the remark that "One side will make you grow taller, and the other side will make you grow shorter."

> *Alice remained looking thoughtfully at the mushroom for a minute, trying to make out which were the two sides of it; and, as it was perfectly round, she found this a very difficult question. However, at last she stretched her arms round it as far as they would go, and broke off a bit of the edge with each hand.*

*"And now which is which?" she said to her-
self, and nibbled a little of the right-hand bit to try
the effect: the next moment she felt a violent blow
underneath her chin; it had struck her foot!*

*She was a good deal frightened by this very
sudden change, but she felt that there was no time
to be lost, as she was shrinking rapidly; so she set
to work at once to eat some of the other bit. Her
chin was pressed so closely against her foot, that
there was hardly room to open her mouth; but she
did it at last, and managed to swallow a morsel of
the left-hand bit.*

And so she grew much taller. One may well wonder what
modern miracle drugs could have been in Alice's bottle
labelled "DRINK ME" and in the little cakes marked
"EAT ME."

Leaving aside science and fantasy and returning to
the realm of the mundane, let us briefly consider the New
York Mycological Society's dinner on December 12,
1965, as reported in *The New York Times*. The forty-five
members scout fields and woods for mushrooms and,
remarked the *Times*, "manage to survive for a banquet
once a year." On this occasion they ate, among other
more usual foods, the matsutake mushroom, a native of
Japan which, because all fungi must be cooked soon after
gathering, they had previously tasted only from imported
cans. However, the composer, John Cage, had found the
matsutake in Oregon and arranged for air shipment of a
quantity, "provided the rabbits don't get to them first."
One of the founders of the group, Guy Nearing, commented wisely on the fate of the mycologist: "Most experts
eventually die of mushroom poisoning because they get
over-confident." The evening ended with the anthem com-
posed by Walton Multer and Hugh Aitken:

*Deep, deep in the murky shadows,
There where the slime mold creeps,*

*With joy the stout mycologist*
*His pallid harvest reaps.*
*Mycology! Great goddess of decay!*

So we can readily see, as Alice did, that though the mushroom cap is round, there *are* two sides to it. Dioscorides put it succinctly, if not very helpfully: "Either they are edible or they are poisonous."

# $\mathcal{N}$ightshades

## Solanaceae

$I$f you take the famous drug plants, deadly nightshade, henbane, jimsonweed, mandrake, tobacco, include with them the food plants, potato, tomato, red and green peppers, eggplants, and then add the ornamentals, petunia, Chinese lantern, apple of Peru, cup-flower and others, you must admit you have a family of rather dazzling variety and extraordinary importance in its value to mankind. Its name is nightshade but the deadly nightshade has its own genus, *Atropa*; other plants which are popularly called by the family name—black nightshade and woody nightshade—belong to the genus *Solanum*. So do the potato and the eggplant, but they are not called nightshades, regardless of the traces of toxic material in them.

The nightshades were generally called *strychnos* (from which we have derived the word strychnine) by the writers of ancient Greece and Rome, and with them they often mixed *Atropa belladonna* and *Mandragora*, because of the similar leaves, berries and poisons. But they could distinguish three types of nightshades, for which they had common names, rather vague as aids to today's scholars. Of them Theophrastus wrote, "one is edible and like a cultivated plant, having a berry-like fruit, and there are

*Solanum nigrum*

two others, of which one is said to induce sleep, the other to cause madness, or, if it is administered in a larger dose, death." Elsewhere, of the first of these he said that it "is also eaten raw, and some in former times considered it worth growing in the gardens." This is none other than the black nightshade (*Solanum nigrum*) or, as it may be called when growing in American gardens, wonder-berry or garden huckleberry.

Pliny mentions the three *strychnos* varieties and, referring to Celsus, even writes in one place *"solanum"*— our modern generic name for it—saying that "It has repressive and cooling properties." Other properties he bestowed on the plants were their value in treating gallstones, kidney ailments, itch; their use for poison on spear points and for those who "wish to play the inspired prophet, and to be publicly seen raving in unpretended madness"; and he says of one that it is "soporific, and kills quicker even than opium." He is slightly more explicit in another passage which informs us that one dose of this nightshade "plays tricks with the sense of shame, speaking of hallucinations and realistic visions; that a double dose causes downright insanity; any addition moreover to the dose bringing instant death."

Those who have studied the old texts can identify certain definite species as we know them, but that need not concern us much here. Centuries later the names and descriptions of plants were somewhat more classified (though still awaiting the work of Linnaeus) and Gerard, with other sixteenth century herbalists, was able to organize many of them into reasonably sound relationships. He wrote of woody nightshade (*S. dulcamara*), giving it its more common name of bittersweet, and of black nightshade (*S. nigrum*), as well as of "Madde Apples" (*S. insanum*).

The black nightshade was introduced into this country as a garden ornamental and is now widespread as a naturalized plant growing in woods, fields, damp low ground or rubbish heaps. It is a delightful herb for those who admire diminutive flowers and plants. It grows about a foot high in a bushy clump: the green leaves have wavey notches around them; the white flowers are drooping, five-pointed stars with yellowish curved cones (the stamens, with anthers fused) projecting from the centers. The flowers turn into green, then black, berries.

Although the leaves and berries contain solanine, a poisonous substance, some people have treated them as food with no harmful effects—after cooking them. In the Dutch East Indies and some other places, the leaves have been used as a potherb for many years and the ripe berries have been cooked in many lands, including North America, in preserves and pies with no ill effects. Apparently sufficient heat will drive out the poison. Some decades ago, in the hope of developing a truly edible fruit, Luther Burbank experimented for years trying to produce a substitute for blueberries from one of these nightshades —but without success. Despite the many testimonials of the harmless nature of the ripe berries when cooked, many people, especially children, have been poisoned by the black nightshade's raw berries. As something safely edible, this "wonder-berry" or "garden huckleberry" must be regarded with some suspicion.

Woody nightshade (*S. dulcamara*) is also an introduced plant which has become naturalized, particularly in the eastern half of the United States. It is also known as European bittersweet, to distinguish it from the native American (false, or climbing) bittersweet (*Celastrus scandens*), which is such a welcome plant for winter decorations and flower arrangements. In the fall the leaves of the American bittersweet shrivel and drop from the woody stems, leaving only clusters of bright crimson berries with a sort of collar formed by the split orange-yellow seed capsules. Animals have been poisoned by browsing on the leaves which, with the berries, are thought to contain a poison called euonymin.

European bittersweet, or woody nightshade, is rather similar to the American plant but is not generally as large, though, given support, such as thickets, hedgerows or fences through which to straggle, it can reach to eight feet. The woody stems near the base put out long trailing branches which crawl and creep through and over anything that will hold them up. The leaves, dark green or even purplish, have an ovate shape, something like an elf's pointed hat, and often at the leaf's base there appear two opposite leaflets, as if the elf wore twirled mustaches or a bow-tie. The flowers, emerging from the ends of the new branches, grow in loose clusters on long stems and are blue, deep violet or purple stars, centered by the bright yellow, fused stamens, like sharpened goose quills. Some years ago I found many charming specimens of this nightshade near the stream which flowed past my studio at Yaddo in Saratoga Springs, New York; one cannot really be too much alarmed by poison in such a tiny brilliant star, so pert, reticent and delicate, and yet incisive. Still, the poison is there. The pretty flowers mature into green berries, which later turn red and cling to the plant, as the berries of the American bittersweet do, after the leaves have fallen.

Bittersweet is a sort of inverted translation of the varietal name, *Dulcamara* ("sweet-bitter"), and though the quack medicine man in Donizetti's opera, *L'Elisir d'Amore*, is named Dr. Dulcamara, there is nothing to indicate, in his musical spiel, that he mixed nightshade drugs in his potions. In his recital of their uses he reminds one of the early herbalists, especially Culpeper, but his "elixir of love" was nothing but bordeaux wine. We cannot expect, however, that the plant, *S. dulcamara*, will prove an elixir to us in its raw, unprocessed, unprescribed state. Nor will its close relative, black nightshade; though that other relative, deadly nightshade, seems to have produced some exhilarating, if often fatal, reactions.

But these two nightshades—the black and the woody —while they do have medicinal properties, are not as useful as the other plant. They contain a poison called solanine, which is, frighteningly, "a glycoside, an alkaloid, a saponin, and a steroid" all at once.[1] Like deadly nightshade it paralyzes the nervous system to a degree— though not affecting the voluntary muscles—but it has no effect on the involuntary muscles of the eyes. It is a mild narcotic, as was known by the Welsh physicians of Myddrai around the thirteenth century; they had a recipe for an anodyne used in extracting a tooth. It sounds sensible but its preparation is complex, involving boilings, steeping and strainings of the root and berries of *S. nigrum* with vinegar and drying the product to a powder, which could be used to deaden the nerves of a tooth.

Solanine also acts as a heart depressant; it slows the breathing, and can result in delirium, convulsions and death. Properly administered by a physician it can be beneficial for stimulating the kidneys, for skin eruptions, rheumatism and various respiratory ailments. Though the plants have their uses, especially in homeopathic medicine, they have been rather by-passed by the new drug-plant researchers in favor of more profitable relatives.

[1] Kingsbury, *Deadly Harvest*, p. 75.

# Poison Ivy and Poison Oak
### Rhus, or Toxicodendron, radicans, quercifolia, diversiloba

# Poison Sumac
### Rhus Vernix

*T*hese plants are inaccurately described by the word "poison" and are included here because they are widespread over this land and annually cause much suffering to those who come into contact with them. The best description of them in relation to their affliction of the human race is allergenic; that is, along with certain other plants, they secrete or produce a substance to which some people are allergic. In the case of the poison ivies, this means almost all people; in the case of another allergenic plant, ragweed, the number is considerably smaller.

None of the viney or shrubby members of the poison ivy family is likely to be planted purposely in one's flower garden, though I have recently heard that some had been offered as pot plants for the home in an English flower catalogue. But these objectionable, though pretty, plants may easily turn up in a garden; the seeds or roots may be carried in with a load of leaf mold, or rich dirt, to be worked into a poorer soil. Or the roots may creep underground from adjoining woodlands or neglected property.

The poison ivies are natives of the United States and

*Rhus Vernix*

southern Canada and have not appealed to most outsiders as something to introduce into their countries. However, they may have been accidentally introduced into Italy a few years ago by the poet, Ezra Pound, when he ordered a shipment of Vermont maple trees sent to his daughter's estate near Tirolo with the idea that maple syrup might be a good agricultural industry for the Italians. The soil around the tree roots seems to have held poison ivy roots and those of trumpet vine, and while the maples did not adapt to their new Latin surroundings, the vines did and are now climbing joyously and brightly from the field below up the high, stone foundation walls of the old Brunnenburg Castle.

Poison ivy is sometimes mistaken for the harmless Virginia creeper. A rule-of-thumb distinction is based on comparison to the normal human skeleton. The leaf of the creeper, like the human hand, has five fingers; the leaves of poison ivy and poison oak have only three fingers —abnormal, and therefore dangerous. The various members of the rash-causing genus *Rhus* have a devilish way of turning seductively scarlet in the fall and must be watched for when gathering autumn foliage.

Almost everyone, it seems, has at some time had an encounter with one of the irritating plants of this family and has suffered from violent itching and blisters. Some people claim immunity but they should be wary—the plant which spared them may have been in too poor condition to exert its influence. But few of us, I imagine, ever knew—or cared—that what caused the inflammation seems to be a yellowish oil called urushiol, which is in the leaves, bark, roots, flowers and fruits of the plants. Solutions to apply to the hands, face, etc., as a poison preventive are sold in drugstores and may or may not be effective. The allergen needs only about ten minutes to establish the skin reaction. So, if contact with the plants has occurred, the affected parts should be washed as soon as possible with hot water and strong alkali soap (such as laundry soap), lathering and rinsing several times. If the rash appears, try not to scratch, as doing so spreads the particles of urushiol; the fluid in the blisters does not carry the allergen. There are numerous recipes for relieving the pain and the itching, and almost anyone you know will tell you a different one. The simplest is a poultice using baking soda or Epsom salts in water, but it might be best to ask your doctor.

Blandishments to the poison ivy will get you nowhere, as need not be pointed out, but years ago the Cherokee Indians hopefully tried them, for whenever they were near the plant they addressed it as "my friend." If the plant was unfriendly, their cure for the poisoning was to rub the beaten flesh of a crawfish on the inflammation, but this isn't a feasible treatment these days.

If you are a real woodsman, like Euell Gibbons, you may be able to counteract the poison by rubbing the exposed parts with a handful of succulent jewelweed (*Impatiens biflora*)—known also as touch-me-not and snapwood—which he says always grows near poison ivy.[1] He also describes the acquired immunity attributed to eating the early spring leaves, three daily for three weeks. But neither he nor I recommend this practice because of variables in susceptibility.

The plants of the genus *Rhus* should not be burned in an attempt to eradicate them, as smoke can carry the allergen. I remember a short story in which a man murders another by the ingenious use of the smoke from poison ivy.

Poison sumac is a shrub or small tree and can be distinguished from the harmless scarlet sumac in several ways. The leaflets of each leaf lack sharply pointed edges and are often turned upward from the petiole. The petiole itself is red, and the fruit is a drooping panicle of white or

[1] Euell Gibbons, *Stalking the Wild Asparagus* (New York, David McKay Company, 1962), p. 283–85.

yellow drupes, instead of the pyramidal panicle of velvety crimson drupes in the more familiar innocent sumac. Mrs. Trollope, describing her tour of the United States in 1830, remarked of the poison sumac: "Another pretty shrub . . . is the poison alder. It is well that its noxious qualities are very generally known, for it is most tempting to the eye by its delicate fringe-like bunches of white flowers. Even the touch of this shrub is poisonous, and produces violent swelling."

Less familiar and widespread, because it is a fairly recent introduction, is the Japanese lacquer-tree (*Rhus verniciflua*) from which urushiol was first isolated. Some people are even allergic to black lacquer-ware, which is finished with the product of this tree. Another member of the family, restricted to southern pine-lands, Florida, and the West Indies, is poison-wood or coral sumac (*Rhus Metopium toxiferum*), whose leaves are rather oval and whose fruit is orange-colored.

Two other allergenic plants might well be mentioned here—ragweed and goldenrod. There is nothing attractive about the various species of ragweed except, ironically, the name of their genus—*Ambrosia*. But there is nothing ambrosial about them, even in name, to sufferers from hayfever. Though no one would cultivate ragweed, many people do admire the grace and brilliance of goldenrod. They gather it, if they are not allergic to it, from fields and roadsides for flower vases, or transplant it in a barren sunny corner of the garden.

In the sixteenth century, when more plants were assumed to have medicinal virtues than were known to be poisonous, goldenrod, having been newly discovered in the American colonies, was thought to possess the power to stanch bleeding of wounds and its dried blossoms were sold for high prices. John Gerard, the great botanist of those days, wrote: "in my remembrance I have known the dry herbe which came from beyond the sea sold in

Bucklersbury in London for halfe a crowne an ounce. But since it was found in Hampstead wood, even as it were at our townes end, no man will give halfe a crowne for an hundred weight of it: which plainely setteth forth our inconstancie and sudden mutabilitie, esteeming no longer of any thing, how pretious soever it be, than whilest it is strange and rare." Gerard then berates the "phantasticall Physitions," who are always seeking new and foreign remedies, in the hope of bringing "these new fangled fellowes backe againe to esteeme better of this admirable plant than they have done, which no doubt have the same vertue now that then it had, although it growes so neere our own homes in never so great quantity." The medicinal virtue of goldenrod is indeed the same as it always was, which appears to be nil, despite the good words of the good John Gerard.

Among the many other plants to which some people may be allergic or which can cause dermatitis, some of the more common are the ailanthus tree (or "tree of heaven" —the tree which "grows in Brooklyn"), juniper, primrose, rue and certain of the plants discussed elsewhere in the book for more genuinely poisonous properties.

# Pokeweed

## Phytolacca americana

*I*n view of its appearance, habit, history and virtues, poke is unjustly called a weed, and yet its reputation and treatment in most parts of this country are as a weed. Since it loves to spring up in newly cleared lands, along cultivated fields and in any rich open soil, it is possible that it would appear in almost any but a city garden and be routed out as a weed because of its rather rank growth. But one of its most gallant contemporary defenders, Euell Gibbons, says, "I have seldom seen a poke plant I wanted removed."

His point is basically well taken because, though the plant contains poisons, it is also a delicious food if properly prepared. To indicate this, its name in the early days of the South was "poke sallet" and it is still called "poke salad" there. Its other common names of scoke, garget, pigeonberry and inkberry make it no more attractive. And it must not be confused with Indian poke, which is white, or false, hellebore.

The American Indians and, following their example, the early explorers and settlers, used the true poke as both food and medicine. This dual usage of the "weed" has continued to the present day. The young sprouts can now

*Phytolacca americana*

be found in the spring at greengrocers in the South and in certain parts of Pennsylvania, while in southern Europe and North Africa poke is popular enough to be cultivated as a vegetable. Medicinally, the root is very powerful and, because of its narcotic effect and physical resemblance, has been used as an adulterate to belladonna. The more obvious effect of the root, the most poisonous part, which like the rest of the plant contains an alkaloid called phytolaccine, is cathartic, emetic and purgative. Only the young spring sprouts, the new leaves and, possibly, the berries

(some children have been poisoned by them) have a
small enough amount of poison to be expelled by boiling
it off. But if eaten incautiously, death could result from
the paralyzing action of narcosis on the lungs. One medicinal application of the plant, as a relief for cancer (which
is debatable), has left the plant with the uninviting folk
name of cancer root.

Poke, indigenous to North American, is our only
member of a very small family of plants, though there are
others like it in the tropics of this hemisphere. A relative
which grows in China is also used, after blanching, as
food. It is a perennial and the root grows larger each year,
reaching the circumference, at the top, of a man's thigh.
This breadth at the top, just under the soil, dwindles below
into a sort of tap root, so that the form of the white-fleshed
root is similar to a gigantic golf tee. The new sprouts
spring from the outer edges of the "saucer" of the root,
and grow up into hollow stalks with widely branching
stems, which reach a height of six to ten feet. The leaves,
elliptical, pointed, and often as long as ten inches, grow
alternately on the stalks and stems, and—one of the plant's
oddities—the racemes of whitish-greenish flowers grow
from the stems opposite the elbow of the leaves and
mature into berries which are at first green and then ripen
into black-purple. Even more odd, or attractive, is the red
or purple color of the succulent stems, especially after the
autumn cold has killed the leaves, and the deep red stalks,
hanging with dark purple berries, are etched against the
landscape.

When poke was introduced into Europe it was
valued as much as an ornamental plant—think of the
novelties from the tropics which we cherish today in our
homes and which are really weeds in their own habitat—
as it was as a vegetable. It is indeed a notable plant visually, with its size, its great leaves, its red-colored stems
and stalks and its drooping racemes of berries. But while

it has been taken to the bosom of some Europeans as a vegetable, it has been, in this country, cast out both as an ornamental and as a food.

European enthusiasm for the plant, especially for the coloring ability of the thick berry juice, which, being apparently harmless, had been used to dye candies and cake frosting, led to the tinting of port wine. In his *History of Esculent Plants* (1783) Charles Bryant reported: "The Portugueze had formerly a trick of mixing the juice of the berries with their red wines, in order to give them a deeper colour; but as it was found to debase the flavour, the matter was presented to his Portugueze Majesty, who ordered all stems to be cut down yearly before they produced flowers, thereby to prevent any further adulteration." Just the same, the delight in the plant as a vegetable remained paramount, and while it is a weed to most of us, to others it is a delicious dish.

For culinary purposes—unless you want to be poisoned—only the very young shoots and leaves should be used. The sprouts should be no longer than six inches, and used while they are still green, for red-purple in the rind indicates the presence of lingering poison. With baby leaves curling together at the top, the shoots resemble asparagus, and when cooked are almost indistinguishable in taste from it. Care must be taken that no bit of the root stock clings to the stalks. Authorities recommend boiling the shoots in lots of water, pouring it off, then simmering them in less water with salt and butter, or other fatty seasoning, before serving.

The very young leaves can be cooked in the same way as a potherb and the stalks can be made into pickles. Euell Gibbons gives recipes for all these uses of the plant, as well as for fried poke, but neither he nor other writers today recommend making pies or tarts of the berries, as earlier authors and country people have done.

If someone develops a craving for this "wild potherb

par excellence," it is possible to grow it through the winter in a cellar. Both Gibbons and Fernald and Kinsey explain in detail how this is done—the long roots are cut to fit into a box of soil and after a sharp freeze moved into a warm basement. "This," writes Gibbons, "is to fool the plants into believing that winter has passed, and that it is time to start growing again. It is a scurvy trick, but it works." Fernald and Kinsey report that twenty medium-sized roots will give a weekly supply for three months to a family of six.

In reading Mr. Gibbons one begins to love poke and long for a dish of it, but he does not try to disguise its danger as a poison. The alkaloid, phytolaccine, and other still unidentified toxic compounds course through the veins of the plant, but are apparently little concentrated in the new growth and can be dissipated by cooking. The root is the most potent, the berries the least, and yet human beings have died after eating them.

# The Indoor Garden and Miscellany

# The Indoor Garden

*F*ifty years ago most of the dwellings in the United States—to say nothing of the rest of the world—did not have the not entirely unalloyed blessings of "central heating," in whose tropical temperatures most Americans now spend their winters, with resultant colds, coughs and worse respiratory ailments; just as fifteen years ago not many spent their summers in arctic-chilled rooms, also with resultant colds, sniffles and coughs. In those ancient days before steam heat, gas space heaters, panel heat or whatever type of heat now suffocates most homes, few plants were grown indoors. In fact, most plants were *supposed* to be growing outdoors in the ground and if you wanted them inside you cut the flowers and put them in a vase. The home today, especially in the large cities, has had to convert itself into a substitute outdoors for those who love growing plants and flowers, since most city-dwellers have no plot of earth to call their own. With our sub-tropical, though dry (electrical devices are available to remedy that), year-round climate, we can grow anything we have money, space and time for.

Our parents and grandparents, with a problem of

how to heat any room comfortably, had hardly any plants in the house during winter except such hardy growers as the ferns—Boston, maidenhair, asparagus—the screw pine (*Pandanus*), corn plant (*Dracaena*), various kinds of rubber plants, small palms or palmettos, aspidistra, and *Sansevieria*—snake plant or, as I always heard it spoken of in the South, "mother-in-law's tongue." There might be a few pots of pelargoniums (usually called geraniums), and the annual pots of hyacinth, narcissus and other bulbs being forced for late winter bloom, such as we usually buy from the florist today.

With the artificial climate available in our homes, one can grow indoors any plant on earth if the dimensions of his living quarters will accommodate it. However, much of the enthusiasm for plants in the city home arises from the basic plainness and drabness of so many of them (being assembly-line produced), and an understandable longing of man, in an unnatural heap of stones and metal and pressures, for the sweet natural life of vegetation. Some of the people caught up in this metropolitan sterility are lucky enough to have pleasant gardens in the rear of their houses, either private or communal; others have their own high and dizzily suspended small balconies or, if more fortunate, solid broad terraces, which can be turned to advantage, horticulturally, with big pots, tubs, planters, or built-in beds for plants. In these outdoor situations, the ornamentals will be those which might be grown in any real garden in the region, but choices must be severely restricted to those plants able to withstand the rigors of the usual urban atmosphere. Most of these have already been discussed in the section on general garden plants. For the majority of city-dwellers, however, a different and, in many cases, a new kind of plant is involved.

Today plants serve a second purpose indoors—not necessarily that of forming the limited garden of a flower lover, but of becoming architecture, the decoration of a room or a relief to severe unadorned angles and acres of blank walls. The plants used in such instances are ordinarily large, tree-like or tall, shrubby growths, and appear in the lobbies of new buildings, banks, office reception rooms and spacious offices, not to mention the stark "modern" apartments. Indeed, the plants themselves may be so modern as to be fabricated of plastic and impervious to temperatures, feeding, growth and change—and even human interest. They are spoken of, by decorators I gather, as "accents." But though some of their "accents," if living, may be poisonous, we need not be concerned with those premises, for no one *lives* in them, people only pass through.

For their own homes city-dwellers, as has already been suggested, strongly favor many of the flowering bulbs toward the end of a nasty, bleak winter, and most of these have been discussed in earlier pages. Also, previously treated and prominent as plants for the indoor—or window—garden are daphne, oleander, box, azaleas (which are much the same as rhododendron), and English ivy.

Decorative though this last plant can be, it always, when in a pot, brings upon me a feeling of sadness. For I remember, in my first years in New York, how many of my friends of those days had bought small pots of ivy to put in their cramped residential hotel rooms as a contact with the natural, real world they had left. I bought them too, and other plants, but they could not long survive the heat and fumes. Poison, yes, but in times such as those, a bright tuft of English ivy on the table or the bureau was an affirmation of life, of the future, of roots not lost—all without reference to the plant's classical symbolism—simply something growing and green. I doubt that this feeling exists in the "talented," the "intellectual" young people in cities today; I doubt that many of them know one plant from another, or even think of plants as such, which is a pity and a mark of their own limitations.

Given the year-round warm climate of most American dwellings, it is not surprising that many delicate plants, formerly seen only in the greenhouses of botanical gardens, are now offered in the shops and catalogues for any interested flower-lover. They are, of course—in order to be attractive the whole year—not usually the herbaceous and deciduous plants of the temperate zones, but rather the perpetually green ones of the tropics. They come in ever larger and more varied shipments from Africa, India, the West Indies, the East Indies, and the equatorial countries of South America. These regions are the happy hunting grounds of modern searchers for unknown plant drugs. Many of the plants offered as pot plants for our homes are new to us, as well as to specialists who might analyze them for possible poisons. Many, however, are already known to be poisonous; others, because of close relationship to proven toxic genera, must be treated with suspicion. Children must be cautioned not to put any part of any of the house plants into their mouths; the flowers, the foliage, the bulbs and roots are more readily at hand in a confined city apartment and a restless and bored child may have more drive to experiment than he would if greater freedom and independence were possible for him. The advice of Dr. Howard C. Mofenson, director of the Nassau County (New York) Poison Control Center should be everyone's guide: "Any plant unless known to be edible must be considered toxic."

Aside from the more than a dozen plants discussed earlier in greater detail, there is at least another dozen, commonly grown in window gardens, which are known to be harmful to the human body. One of these, and one of the most dangerous for children because of its attractive flowers and sweet scent, I had meant to place in my final section, as a native wild vine so handsome that many people have transplanted it to their gardens. Last fall I discovered that it is being recommended as a pot plant for indoors.

This is the yellow (or Carolina) jessamine (*Gelsemium sempervirens*), which grows in woods and mountains from Virginia across the South into Central America. Its yellow trumpets of fragrant flowers, with the five lobes curling back, and its pointed glossy evergreen leaves account for much of its appeal. The roots, leaves and flowers contain the alkaloids gelsemine and gelseminine, which are similar in action to strychnine. Grazing animals are frequently poisoned by yellow jessamine and the history of children poisoned by merely sucking the nectar from the blossoms goes back a hundred years. In fact, bees have been poisoned by it and, in turn, have poisoned their honey. The effect of the poison, which is evident rather quickly, is to produce muscular weakness, lowering of the temperature, slowing of respiration and, if enough has been swallowed, paralysis, failure of the lungs, and death. Years ago many poisonings resulted from the use of the roots as an adulterant to flavor gin. The drugs have been used in medicine for many diseases.

A favorite house plant which is particularly tempting to children is Jerusalem cherry (*Solanum pseudo-capsicum*), a nightshade, prized most for its pretty red or orange berries. They are highly toxic, containing solanine and two more alkaloids. Another favorite, belonging to a very poisonous family, is crown of thorns (*Euphorbia splendens* or *milii*), which many people erroneously deem a cactus because of the sharp spines set in the ridged, gray, woody stems. But it is really one of the spurges, which are filled with a milky and too often, as in this case, poisonous juice. Of course, when a plant is so spiny that one can hardly handle it without being sorely pricked by its thorns, one is not going to be much tempted to bite into it. For this reason I think we need fear as little harm from the crown of thorns as from the spiny species of agave and yucca which are now being promoted as indoor plants for their stark "modern" lines but which may, like some of their relatives, contain saponin compounds injurious to the human system.

Many *Euphorbias* are popular as house plants, because of colorful foliage or flowers, or dramatic line and form; some of these—the candelabra cactus and the pencil tree, for instance—have been mentioned in the pages on snow-on-the-mountain. By no means all the spurges are poisonous, but with such a dangerously popular family one should be wary of even those cousins which have no definite black marks against them yet. Among these are the crotons, those handsome shrubs and trees with long narrow leaves, vividly marked with a wide range of colors—yellow, red, white, purple. They come from the Malayan peninsula and the Pacific islands but are quite naturalized in the West Indies and the American semitropical regions; they are always available in flower shops but are tricky to sustain in good health for very long in the usual apartment. This plant is not the one which provides the deadly croton oil—that is still another of the spurges—but is classified as *Codiaeum variegatum* or *pictum*. Two attractive members of the *Euphorbiaciae,* not so well known and more difficult to cultivate indoors —plants whose possible toxic nature is uncertain but whose foliage and flowers no one should chew—are the East Indian chenille plant (*Acalypha hispida*), with green leaves and long drooping spikes of tiny red or purple flowers; and copperleaf (*Acalypha wilkesiana*), with bracts of fluffy red "flowers" and broad scarlet or variegated leaves.

We might well extend our suspicions to all species of the arum family (*Araceae*), since so many of them are proven to be poisonous and so many are popular house plants. Apparently all the arums contain oxalates, which cause a harmful calcium deficiency in the blood, or crystals of calcium oxalate, which drive into the tissues of the mouth, tongue and throat, producing severe irritation and burning, and a swelling which can close the throat and thus suffocate the victim. Well known wild and dangerous examples are the cuckoopint (*Arum maculatum*), jack-in-the-pulpit (*Arisaema atrorubens*), skunk cabbage (*Symplocarpus foetidus*), and wild calla (*Calla palustris*). None of these, of course, is a pot plant; the potted calla lily sold by florists belongs to the genus *Zantedeschia,* but is, nevertheless, an arum. As to other members of the family, many species of *Philodendron, Caladium* and *Alocasia,* hothouse favorites from the orient, also have the toxic properties described above.

One of the more frequently encountered plants of the arum family, both in homes and in public rooms, is called by the common name of dumb cane in its native lands of the West Indies and South America. Most people probably know it by its generic name of *Dieffenbachia.* It rises on a thick woody stem to a height of three to six feet, with large, oblong, pointed leaves, spotted with deeper shades of green or with white or yellowish blotches, spreading out at the top. It contains crystals of calcium oxalate whose action on the mouth and throat, inflaming and swelling them so as to deprive a person who bites into the plant of the power of speech, accounts for its name of dumb cane. It has been a cause of serious impairment to the health and even of death. As evidence of its irritant and crippling effects, consider the recent case of a woman who, in intense pain, with swollen face, and barely able to speak intelligibly, entered a hospital in Cleveland, Ohio. She had bitten, for some reason, into the stalk of a *Dieffenbachia,* but had almost immediately spat out the pulp and the juices in her mouth and swallowed nothing. But it took two weeks for her to recover fully.

Other popular arums found on the indoor garden shelf which, while not definitely known to be poisonous, should be regarded as possible producers of harmful amounts of calcium oxalates, are Chinese evergreen (*Aglaonema*) whose habit of growth is very similar to that of dumb cane; *Monstera deliciosa*, which seems to be considered a giant philodendron by most people; the brilliant weird *Anthurium* (from Greek meaning "tail flower"); the similar but far less colorful spathe flower (*Spathiphyllum floribundum*); and the viney plants called pothos (*Scindapsus*).

Various species of *Cyclamen*, a member of the primrose family originating in central and southern Europe and Asia Minor, are hardy plants in temperate regions and one, *C. persicum*, is a common potted plant in florists' shops. With good reason: a mound of cool fresh heart-shaped leaves, variegated in shades of green or marbled with silver-white, rises from the rim of the pot on dull russet stems, and above it, also on red-brown stems, a froth of nodding, white or rose flowers, their petals sharply turned back. Each blossom suggests a shooting star and indeed shooting star (*Dodecatheon*) is the name of a closely related native American kinsman.

Cyclamen was the classical name of the plant, whose root, wrote Theophrastus: "is used for suppurating boils; also as a pessary for women and, mixed with honey, for dressing wounds; the juice for purgings of the head . . . it also conduces to drunkenness, if one is given a draught of wine in which it has been steeped. They say also that the root is a good charm for inducing rapid delivery and as a love potion; when they have dug it up, they burn it, and then, having steeped the ashes in wine, make little balls like those made of wine lees which we use as soap." In that distant era cyclamen was a valuable plant in medicine; Pliny tells us that it is useful in treating eye diseases, nasal catarrh, jaundice, burns, running ulcers and as a laxative, emmenagogue and extractor of splinters. But he also says that it has "a poisonous quality of its own, and it is said that if a woman with child steps over this root she miscarries." He mentioned three kinds, one of which was called "earth truffle," perhaps because of the tuberous root or because pigs dug it out of the ground to eat, as they do the fungus truffle.

For swine apparently dote on these roots and are not harmed by them. So, to Gerard, the plant was known as sow-bread and one of its virtues was that of an aphrodisiac, "Being beaten and made up into trochisches, or little flat cakes, it is reported to be a good amorous medicine to make one in love." Culpeper continued the ancient tradition of the plant's uses: "The root is very forcing, used to bring away the birth and the secundines, and to provoke the menses. The juice is commended against vertiginous disorders of the head, used in form of an errhine; it is good against cutaneous eruptions." And Abraham Cowley summarized for all subsequent homeopaths the knowledge of the Greeks and Romans about cyclamen:

> *My virtue dries all ulcerous running sores,*
> *And native softness to the skin restores.*
> *My pow'r hard tumours cannot, if I list*
> *Either by water, or with fire, resist.*
> *Of scars by burning caus'd, I clear the face,*
> *Nor let small pox the countenance disgrace. . . .*
> *In my fire that false gold the jaundice, I*
> *Consume (true gold scarce does more injury). . . .*
> *I of the gout remove the very seed*
> *And all the humours which that torment breed,*
> *Thorns, splinters, nails, I draw, who wondering*
>     *stand*
> *How they could so come forth without a hand.*

Official medicine has little regarded the cyclamen in spite of the active substances in its root and juices, substances which seem to produce reactions in the body similar to saponin.

More favorably regarded by physicians is the drug

extracted from another beautiful and quite spectacular house plant of the cactus family. This is the night-blooming cereus (*Selenicereus grandiflorus* and *pteranthus*), introduced from the West Indies and Central and South America. It has thick, fleshy, ribbed, spiny stems, blue-green or darkening to purple, from which long buds emerge and on a winter night open rapidly into huge dazzling complex white flowers and wither within a few hours. This flower and its behavior are impossible to describe satisfactorily; one has to see to grasp the beauty and mystery they project.

In the nineteen thirties when the place where I lived was still hardly large enough to be called a city, and before the draft and subsequent war separated many of us, a few friends organized, very informally, a Night-blooming Cereus Club. A charter member, the most prominent one today, and, I should say, the president of this club was Eudora Welty. On the nights when these plants were to bloom—for the date of flowering can be gauged accurately—we would arrange to meet and drive out to call upon those of our acquaintances who owned them. And as the newspapers announced the imminent blossoming of other plants in the homes of various other people, we even called upon strangers. We always found a small group waiting expectantly, as if participating in a rite; we would sit with them and watch the bud tremble and shudder while it unwound its long, slender white petals and spread them before our incredulous eyes as a delicately incised saucer full of froth. Before daylight had come this awesome display of loveliness and of visible unfolding in a flower had shrivelled to a flaccid, soggy mass of gray tissue as unpleasant to see as refuse dropped in a gutter.

When our club members were reunited after the war, the city was too large for us to ring the doorbells of cereus-growing strangers and the papers no longer reported on them. But we still could have the amazing experience, which sets up all sorts of trains of thought, of watching swift flower-openings, as in a Walt Disney nature film, on the patio of a friend who not only gave us drinks and barbecued dinners but had a nearby moonflower vine (*Calonyction aculeatum*). This member of the morning-glory family is really a night-glory and while we drank our bourbon and water under the stars we could almost hear, if we weren't gabbling too loudly, the warning pops, as one after another of the long buds burst and unpleated the flowers into wide, flat white salvers shedding an elusive fragrance.

It may or may not be that the seeds of this vine have the hallucinatory properties, similar to those of the LSD drugs, which have been found in the famous Mexican morning-glory, *ololiuqui*, and even in the cultivated American species, *Ipomea tricolor*; all species of this plant are now under serious investigation. The night-blooming cereus, however, is known to contain substances which are cardioactive, as well as sedative and diuretic, and in excessive amounts have caused hallucinations and mild delirium. The drug extracted from the plant is recognized in official medicine.

For indoor growth a common plant—so common indeed that it grows wild, having escaped from cultivation, in some of the southern states of the United States—is trailing lantana (*Lantana montevidensis*). A good choice for a hanging basket, this shrubby but straggling plant with rosy-lilac flowers was introduced from South America. Other species which form bushes and grow, naturalized, in the temperate zones and have yellow, orange or red flowers, are not used as pot plants. The rather prickly stems and the hairy leaves cause dermatitis in some people and, though they are not exactly appetizing, they have been eaten by grazing stock and have caused serious poisoning. And, as if to prove that there is nothing a toddler will not eat, there are records of a number of cases in which children have been poisoned by lantana. The plant contains a toxin which affects the liver and may, if much of the toxin has been absorbed, produce weakness of the muscles and the circulation.

Potentially harmful flowers often appear in the homes of those who have no special interest in cultivating plants —as birthday gifts, as cheer for the sick or solace for the bereaved, as decorations for some particular celebration, but most frequently at Easter, when spring flowers appeal to nearly everyone, and at Christmas, when almost every home is decked with evergreens. One of the popular presents at Eastertide is a small potted azalea or a cyclamen but, because of the connection of lilies with the season, they are overshadowed by Easter and Madonna lilies, with narcissus, daffodil, lily of the valley and hyacinth trailing as second choices. Next in line are the amaryllises, and favorites are the poisonous bulbs with the lovely flowers, —the red *Nerine* and blood lilies and the white (often with red markings) *Crinum* lily. The last of these handsome plants is a substitute source of the cardiac drug found in squills.

During the Christmas season, again cyclamen may serve as a flower greeting, but the poinsettia—*Euphorbia (Poinsettia) pulcherrima*—has become a traditional one in the years since 1828 when J. R. Poinsett, United States minister to Mexico, found the plant there. The red "flower" of this member of the spurges is actually a whorl of leaves surrounding the tiny beady flowers (male and female) in the center. Children have been fatally poisoned by this plant which is brought into so many homes at Christmas. Other dangerous growth which appears in dwellings, not as pot plants but as holiday decorations to form garlands or wreaths or to adorn mantles, chests and tables, are ivy and various berried vines and boughs. Bittersweet, favored for its contorted, leafless stems and

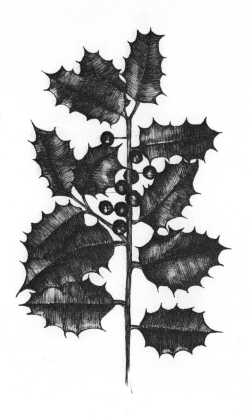

*Ilex opaca*

clusters of orange berries, is usually arranged in a vase without water and has no particular relevance to Christmas. Holly and mistletoe do, however, and are used annually in millions of homes, where the berries may easily fall to the floor, available to even a crawling baby.

Both plants have long histories as sacred symbols in pagan cults. Though Theophrastus had little to say of holly (*Ilex aquifolium*), Pliny prescribed the leaves, berries and roots for a variety of ills, including dysentery and cholera, and quoted Pythagoras as saying the holly flower would freeze water. Also the tree or a stick from it possessed certain magical powers, such as protecting a house from lightning and witchcraft. Holly figured in the Roman celebration of the Saturnalia, which began shortly before Christmas, when people sent each other gifts adorned with evergreen boughs. The tree was used by the Druids, worshippers of sylvan spirits, to adorn their rooms in the winter so as to provide a shelter in the evergreens for the woodland spirits.

In converting pagans to Christianity, the early fathers of the Church had to accommodate their own religion in some degree to the customs of the pagans. So the Saturnalian practice of giving presents, and the Druidical practice of decking the house with evergreens carried over and down the years and became part of the celebration of Christmas. In making such adaptations, it perhaps became necessary to mask or sanctify pagan material. There is a legend that holly grew up wherever Jesus walked on earth, and the thorny leaves and blood-red berries symbolize his crown of thorns and crucifixion. In fact, in the languages of many European countries the name of the tree is "Christ's thorn." Before the time of the Renaissance, it was generally called "Holy tree" in English and this is very likely the origin of the name holly.

The Green Knight, a green-skinned, green-garbed giant, who interrupted King Arthur's Yuletide feasting to challenge Sir Gawain, is probably an ancient nature symbol enacting a battle of the solstices—midwinter and midsummer. The Green Knight, in fact, carried a holly bough. English folk songs of a later period are frequently concerned with the holly and the ivy, and this connection, a sexual symbol, was evident in the choice of holly as the male element and ivy, the "clinging vine," as the female. Certain games and celebrations—choosing the holly-boy or holly-king—were involved and vestiges of them can be found in some traditions and folk songs still known today.[1]

Though the ancients made an aphrodisiac of the berries, and birds eat them without ill effects, holly berries are harmful to children. In homeopathic medicine the leaves have been used "in fomentations for broken bones, and such members as are out of joint," and for catarrh, pleurisy and smallpox. The berries have been recommended for dropsy and other disorders. But they are said to contain a bitter alkaloid called ilicin and are known to be violently emetic and purgative.

Mistletoe (*Viscum album* is the European genus; *Phoradendron flavescens* the American) has much the same history as holly except that it is a true parasite and feeds upon its host. To Pliny it was a poisonous plant, and he gives many scattered antidotes for it—rue, oregano, straight wine and, of all things, radishes. At the same time he could provide many medicinal uses for the plant and he also gave us an account of its significance to the Druids. On the fifth day of the moon, he wrote, it was gathered from the sacred oak "with rites replete with religious awe. . . . This day they select because the moon, though not yet in the middle of her course, already has considerable power and influence; and they call her by a name which signifies, in their language, the all-healing." In the ceremonies two white bulls were sacrificed and a banquet was spread under the trees. At the proper time, "Clad in a white robe the priest ascends the tree, and cuts the mistletoe with a golden sickle." This branch is, of course, the "golden bough" of Sir James G. Fraser, for the European species of mistletoe has a decided yellow cast in the branches and leaves, and the cutting of the bough was a symbolic emasculation of the king who was to be replaced.

[1] The complicated investigations which Robert Graves made in *The White Goddess* include much about the prominence of holly, as well as mistletoe, in ancient legends and history.

*Phoradendron flavescens*

Pliny reported further that the Druids considered
mistletoe an antidote to all poisons and that in a drink it
would make any barren animal fecund. The plant, however, was also associated with magic, as a charm against
evil, and sprigs of it were sent by the priests to announce
the new year. It is no distant leap, except in centuries,
from their use of the plant to ours today.

Although mistletoe was a major ingredient in many
old remedies and is still used in folk medicine in certain
lands, the most successful application of the berries has

been in making birdlime. Its toxins have killed cattle which ate the plant and many cases are recorded of fatal poisoning of children by the berries. They contain, apparently, toxic amines and the effect can be narcotic, a deadening of nervous responses, and a cardiac stimulation. To get these effects in a, perhaps, far less dangerous way, it is best just to kiss underneath a sprig of it.

The three most important Christmas greens—ivy, holly and mistletoe—had all established their ceremonial relevance in pagan customs, and many years ago the Church banned them all as decorations. Holly and ivy have since been forgiven their past associations and are now allowed in churches—many of which have long been covered with ivy anyway. But mistletoe is still forbidden; it is judged too evil a plant even today.

*W*hen I was seven or eight years old I planted my first garden. It was made up of four plants, all in common varieties, whose names began with P—pansies, petunias, phlox and portulaca, which I called moss-rose. This garden came about because down the block from my home there lived the widow of a railroad engineer and she had a front yard quite different from the others in town. Ours, and most of the yards around the neighborhood, were expanses of "lawn"—which, when my brothers had gone to college, I had to mow—with trees and against the house a border of one or another large shrubby flowering plant. Mrs. Wright's front yard was a crude but oriental carpet of color. No patch of lawn was anywhere near; the land in front of the house and alongside, all enclosed with a low white pointed paling fence, was carved into varied segments, marked off to designate paths by diagonally embedded colored bottles, and in the beds formed by these retainers, there bloomed myriad flowers. The surface of the ground was all color in the spring and summer and I am sure I leaned over her fence many a time to admire the display made by those most ordinary plants. At length she gave me the four transplants to start my own garden, though my mother had all sorts of common and less common plants growing. I was assigned a space on the east side of our house where I planted my flowers. None of them, apparently, were poisonous, but a year or so later I became fascinated by the peculiar blossoming habit of four-o'clocks and sowed their seeds in my patch of ground.

The four-o'clock (*Mirabilis jalapa*) grows up quickly into a three-foot herb with widely variegated, scented flowers which open in the late afternoon. I used to try to catch them opening, but was always too early or too late. In the sixteenth century the plant was introduced from Peru into Spain, and Gerard knew it in England as the "Marvell of Peru" and admired it. "We have not as yet," he wrote, "any instructions from the people of India [to him South America was the Indies] concerning the nature or vertues of this plant: the which is esteemed as yet rather for his rareness, beautie, and sweetness of his floures, than for any vertues knowne; but it is a pleasant plant to decke the gardens of the curious." But not, it would seem, pleasant enough to sustain its earlier popularity into the present century. I did not know until recently that this now neglected plant has poisonous roots and seeds which have injured those who ate them.

Another shaking up of my memories of boyhood came recently in my pursuit of vegetable poisons. Somehow, one doesn't like to learn unfavorable facts about plants one has loved, especially those which are very modest, intimate and personal, almost folksy and not showy like a huge orchid. I should expect such flagrant sirens as orchids to be bad inside, but my shy, sweet, unpublicized *Calycanthus*! Even its family is small—only two genera and about six species—and it—*my* calycanthus (*C. floridus* or *fertilis*)—lives in the woods of the southern states except when someone transplants it to his garden plot. Others are found in California and related species grow in China and Japan. Mine was often called, especially by country folk, sweet shrub or Carolina allspice.

It was usually, in gardens where I saw it, a small shrub with dark green ovate leaves, downy underneath, but in its wild state it might be found reaching to ten feet in height. It was certainly such tall shrubs that William Bartram encountered on his botanical travels through the South and whenever he set down the name in his book, which was frequently, he almost always accompanied it with a tribute to the blossoms' major charm, "aromatic Calycanthean groves on the surrounding heights," he wrote, and in other citations the plant received such descriptions as fragrant, odorous, sweet, odoriferous, perfumed.

Although the bark itself is aromatic, the source of the odor in the air is the flowers, dark reddish-brown, with many slender curving petals and a spicy fragrance which, as I recall, seemed to mingle cloves, bananas, mangoes and ginger. But maybe I am lapsing into sentimental hyperbole and leaving aside the accurate reminiscence which should concern us. When the buds of *Calycanthus* had begun to open in the spring, children who had access to them usually arrived at school with one knotted loosely in the corner of a handkerchief (so as not to lose it). Sometimes they brought extra buds to give to friends, for few people seemed to cultivate the wild bush. The odor of *Calycanthus* meant that it would not be long until vacation time. And the students in study hall and classes, sniffing at handkerchief knots and naked buds, could not have seemed more intolerant of the air around them than the ladies and fops of the eighteenth century with their scent bottles, sachets and smelling salts.

If cattle had not eaten the seeds, we might all be in a state of innocence about the plant. But the seeds contain an alkaloid called calycanthine, whose action on the body resembles that of strychnine.

Another beloved plant of my early life, and another harbinger of spring, has only in the past few years been found guilty of poisoning. That is surprising, since the vine—*Wisteria floribunda* and other species—is so common in the United States, north and south. The more popular forms are oriental in origin, but there are indigenous American species. The long racemes, like grape bunches, of blue or white pea blossoms hanging from the just leafing vines, and their sweet odor, easily account for the popularity of wisteria. There have been many cases of children poisoned by eating the pods or seeds, even as few as two. The toxin causes severe disturbances in the digestive system, with vomiting and diarrhea.

Another member of the *Wisteria*'s large family of peas (*Leguminosae*), not a vine but a tree, whose pods produce the same effects, is the *Poinciana*, which grows outdoors in the warm southern states but is sometimes used as a potted shrub in the north. Its attractions are the graceful feathery leaves, like mimosa, and the clustered yellow or red flowers. A related vine which is well known and called plainly sweet pea (*Lathyrus odoratus*) belongs to a genus which, in the past few years, has stirred serious attention in biochemists who are investigating the neuroactive substances in them. These substances are made up chiefly of two separate amine compounds which are found in certain species. Eating sweet pea stems has caused a form of paralysis which has in some instances confined the subject to bed for months. The toxins in some of the plants also affect bone structure detrimentally and those in other plants cause convulsions.

The lupine, a widespread member of the pea family, both wild and cultivated and in many species, is a small shrubby plant, annual or perennial, with attractive, divided palmate leaves and a stalk of blossoms in white, yellow, blue or purple. Some of the species are highly poisonous, especially the pods and the peas inside; others are less dangerous, but knowledge of all species and their alkaloids—thought to be as many as five—is not complete.

It seems that the ancient Egyptians converted the seeds of white lupines into bread meal. Pliny reported that lupines were excellent as food and as medicine for abscesses, black ulcers, worms and other ailments; they also could be made into various beauty treatments to remove pimples, bruises, freckles, etc., and indeed, they "increase the appetite, and remove squeamishness." Much of his record of the value of lupines has continued through Culpeper to the homeopaths of today. However, the uncertainty about the toxic nature of the genus should be sufficient to prevent people eating any part of the plant. It has been reported that of two thousand sheep pastured on a range covered with lupines, half were poisoned by the herb and seven hundred of them died.

How strange that in this leguminous family from which we derive so much food in the form of edible seeds —chick peas, peanuts, lentils, green, lima and kidney beans, green peas and many varieties of field peas—we find at the opposite end of the scale a pea not merely to be cautious of but, because of its concentrated lethal power, actually frightened of. And yet this plant, a vine indigenous to the tropics around the world, has been introduced into Florida where it has escaped and grows wild; and its seeds, in the form of ornaments, hang at the wrists and throats of thousands of women across the country. What an ironically benign common name it has —rosary pea; or closer to the botanical name, precatory bean (*Abrus precatorius*). It seems to have been introduced into Florida for industrial purposes—for the manufacture of necklaces, rosaries, bracelets and other ornaments from the small glossy seeds, part black and part red.

The vine is somewhat like vetch in its twining growth and leaflets, and has red or purple flowers. The seed produced is about half the size of a pencil eraser, and yet one seed, if chewed and swallowed, is enough to kill an adult. Two college girls in the West learned this, to their sorrow, when the necklace which one of them was wearing broke. For some incomprehensible reason, which one cannot explain away as the ignorance of infants, they decided to eat a bead or two, now that the beads were reduced to mere loose seeds.

The poison in the precatory bean is a toxic protein called abrin, which causes in the body the common gastro-intestinal disturbances accompanied by weakness, cold sweats, feeble but rapid pulse, trembling of the hands, and, unless the poison is removed as quickly as possible, death.

Still another vine, an introduction from southern Europe and the Middle East as an ornamental but not in great favor these days, is matrimony vine (*Lycium hali-mifolium* and *chinense*). It might be considered more a shrub than a vine, and its long arching branches could certainly be trimmed and trained to form a shrub. Its second common name, box-thorn, reveals one possible reason—the spiny branches—for its decline in favor as a garden plant. In answer to such neglect it simply made itself at home near the woods to which it had escaped. Its stems are gray, its leaves green on top and gray under-neath, its bell-shaped flowers deep lilac to purple and its fruit, a berry, colored scarlet to orange-red. Its poison, which has stricken cattle and sheep, is an alkaloid much like the hyoscyamine of its family, the nightshades.

But surely one of the most widely escaped vines, especially in the southern states, is honeysuckle. It forms large mounds of twisted, tangled stems and foliage on the edges of old roads, on fences, on bushes and small trees; and on large trees it can raise a thick sheath around the trunk. When the thin trumpet flowers, pale yellow or white or with pink tinges, open, a delicate fragrance drifts through the air. Children—old-time children, that is— love to suck the nectar from the flowers, and luckily it doesn't seem to be harmful, or I should have suffered from it in my childhood, considering how much of the honey I sucked from those blossoms.

While several of the shrubby members of this family (*Caprifoliaceae*) are popular with gardeners, I don't think anyone really cultivates these two sweet-smelling vines (*Lonicera caprifolium* and *L. periclymenum*)—they grow too rankly to control. But one likes to have them around in open spaces where there is room for their comfortable growth. The species called *periclymenum* is known to the English not only as honeysuckle but as the woodbine, which flourishes throughout the British landscape as well as in the lines of British poetry. John Gerard grew honey-suckles, one of which he described in this way, "fair, beautifull, and well smelling floures, shining with a whitish purple colour, and somewhat dasht with yellow, by little and little stretched out like the nose of an elephant."

The vines have been used in medicine by homeopaths from the time of Dioscorides to the present. One is at first astonished at Culpeper's words on the plant: "Take a leaf and chew it in your mouth and you will quickly find it likelier to cause a sore mouth and throat than cure it." However, he saves the day in his next words: "If it be not good for this, what is it good for? It is good for something, for God and nature made nothing in vain." Then follow the astrological analysis and the many uses—for asthma, palsy, freckles, birth pains, and other afflictions. Some of the modern remedies are an infusion of the flowers for bronchitis, an infusion of the leaves as a laxative and the flowers preserved in syrup for asthma. None of the med-icinal uses are official and, though there are few references to it, the substances in the seeds, which are orange or red berries, have been reported to be poisonous to children.

A beautiful blooming plant in many forms, even in the new large-flowered hybrid vines, is the clematis, some-times called virgins-bower. As a member of the buttercup family, which gives us monkshood, larkspur, pasque flower and hellebore, it might well be regarded as a possible producer of poisons. Of the climbing varieties, particularly of *Clematis virginiana*—a well known American species with graceful leaves and fluffy white cymes of flowers—little worse can be said, with our present knowledge, than that it often causes dermatitis in some people. However, a similar species, except that it forms a shrub (*C. recta*), contains an acrid irritant poison. Another low shrub of the family, pheasants-eye or Adonis, which produces red, orange or yellow flowers, is toxic in at least one species. The summer Adonis (*A. aestivalis*; there are also spring and autumn types) has poisoned horses and there are reports of poisoning from other species of the plant.

One of our very common, very hardy, and somewhat unappreciated trailing plants is often called periwinkle or running myrtle (*Vinca major* or *V. minor*). In spite of its pretty blue flowers and its glossy fine leaves, it is usually treated to the designation of "ground cover"—something as inconspicuous as grass. I have always been fond of these poor little plants, a sentiment I seem to share with Chaucer, and have been glad to see them, set in the right spot, beautifying an earthen bank or slope or flowing over the top of a wall in a cool green waterfall, and sad to see them determinedly struggling to survive under layers of dust in city backyards. I have noticed that experienced and professional gardeners do not scorn the plants but use them regularly to set off some more impressive blossoming specimen.

There is an erect species, a low shrub (*Vinca rosea*) with deep rose flowers, which is not so familiar but is commonly called Madagascar periwinkle. All of these periwinkles belong to the dogbane family (*Apocynaceae*), which includes a number of toxic members, such as oleander. And the common periwinkles were used medicinally from the time of Galen and Dioscorides, who prescribed them for diarrhea. Albertus Magnus had a recipe for an aphrodisiac using *Vinca*, "Perwynke when it is beate unto pouder with worms of ye earth wrapped about it and with an herbe called houslyke, it induceth love between man and wyfe if it bee used in their meales."

The greater periwinkle (*V. major*) was reputed to have astringent properties useful in bleeding and congestion, and I suspect that it was leaves of this vine which were pounded into a poultice and bound around my hand when I, a child on the Gulf Coast, was severely pinched by a large crab I had picked up—but not with the proper technique.

Folk medicine, however, seem to have missed the real and exciting virtues of *Vinca*, except for certain oriental groups which used the leaves of *V. rosea* as a treatment for diabetes. The investigation of the effectiveness of this remedy led through almost two decades to dramatic and encouraging discoveries by scientists. The periwinkles, especially *V. rosea*, produce an astonishing number of astonishing alkaloids. The last report was that forty-three different ones had been isolated and these, as scientists proceeded from their known use in diabetes, are now being tested with high hopes and some positive results, as anti-cancer drugs. But no one knows yet how the drugs act upon the human tissues of the body. This is only a beginning, with good results so far, and though no definite outcome is predictable, the *Vinca* derivatives (two prominent ones are called by the names of vincristine and vinblastine) are the only drugs from the higher plant forms currently being tested by the National Cancer Institute. But, since it takes two tons of crushed leaves to produce, at an expense of thousands of dollars, one gram of the extract, *Vinca* may be removed from the class of ornamentals and become primarily a botanical drug-crop plant.[1] A few more popular garden plants, some more

[1] Margaret Kreig, *Green Medicine*, pp. 301–316.

poisonous than periwinkle but none nearly so promising
in benefits to mankind, should be mentioned, even though
there are still scores of others which may be harmful to the
human body. One of the more dangerous plants has
usually been considered a wild native vine, often with a
shrub-like habit, but it is now being offered as a garden
ornamental. This is moonseed (*Menispermum canadense*),
whose fruits have frequently been eaten by children in
the belief that they were wild grapes. They do indeed
resemble grapes in appearance, but not in their bitter
taste or their single seed, shaped like a crescent moon,
inside each drupe. The poison has not been identified.

Burning bush (*Euonymus atropupureus*) grows wild
in the eastern United States but it is much used as an
ornamental shrub, eight to ten feet high, because of its
copper-red foliage in autumn and its red berries. Both
leaves and fruits have caused serious poisoning in children,
resulting in nausea and prostration and, if enough has
been ingested, death. Called spindle tree in Europe,
because the wood is used to make spindles, this plant
supplies several folk remedies in both the Occident and
the Orient.

The fruit of mock orange (*Philadelphus*), a favorite
shrub for its fragrant blossoms and decorative "oranges,"
has poisoned children and its relative in the saxifrage
family, *Hydrangea*, which seems never to have acquired
a common name, can also be dangerous. Because of its
foliage, hydrangea has been valuable to landscape gardeners for massing in clumps—though some growers say
it must be planted to the north or east of a house or wall—
and the big globular cymes of clustered white, pink or
blue flowers have always delighted everyone. The name
of this handsome shrub comes from the Greek meaning
"water-vessel," and it refers to the shape of the cymes as
well as the preference of the plant for growing in marshes.
It requires a lot of water and the leaves begin to droop if
it doesn't get enough. It was in such a moist situation that

William Bartram discovered the native American species, the oak-leaved hydrangea (*H. quercifolia*) in Georgia:

> *It grows in coppices or clumps near or on the banks of rivers and creeks. Many stems usually arise from a root spreading itself greatly on all sides by suckers or offsets. The stems grow five or six feet high, declining or diverging from each other. . . . These flowers are of two kinds: the numerous partial spikes which compose the panicles and consist of a multitude of very small fruitful flowers, terminate with one or more very large, expansive, neutral or mock flowers, standing on a long, slender, stiff peduncle; these flowers are composed of four broad oval petals of segments, of a dark rose or crimson color at first, but as they become older acquire a deeper red or purplish hue, and lastly are of a brown or ferruginous color. These have no perfect parts of generation of either sex, but discover in their center two, three, or four papillae or rudiments. These neutral flowers, with the whole panicle, are truly permanent, remaining on the plant for years, until they dry and decay; the leaves which clothe the plants are very large, pinnatifid or palmated, and serrated or toothed, very much resembling the leaves of some of our oaks.*

The root of hydrangea is used in homeopathic medicine, and the plant does indeed contain toxic substances. Though these poisons have not been isolated or thoroughly understood, one should beware of chewing the leaves or flowers.

A somewhat similar shrub, but not related (it belongs to the honeysuckle family), is the snowball bush (*Viburnum opulus*) which produces flowers like large snowballs, as one would expect. In England it is known as guelder rose and, because of the chemical compounds produced in the plant, has been called cramp bark. A herbal medicine was made from the bark as a remedy for cramps, convulsions and other disorders. The active principle seems to be a glycoside called viburnine and it has a small place in official medicine in some countries.

A large, cool-looking leaf to be avoided as a nibble or a snack is that of the elephant's-ear (*Colocasia*). It will taste bitter and no one, probably, would eat much of it; but it is one of the arum family and can produce reactions similar to those of dumb cane, though perhaps not as severe.

Listing and commenting on more or less dangerous plants could go on—the roots of peony, dahlias and wild blue iris, the leaves of flowering almond, butterfly weed, the flowers or leaves of fringe tree—but they could add little new to the subject of poisonous plants for the general reader. The warnings given by authorities which have been repeated by me should not frighten anyone away from flowers and plants with beautiful foliage but are intended to instruct the reader and enable him to distinguish plants which are very dangerous, those which are less so, and those which are presumed to be harmless. After all, as has already been pointed out, even our customary meal-time vegetables contain small amounts of toxic substances. We could not live without plants, nor could most of the other animals on this earth. The vegetable kingdom is virtually the keystone which supports the house of life. Our duty is not to fear it, but to understand its potentials. It can nourish us and heal us; it can also afflict us and kill us. Even as we delight in the flowers which it provides, we must be aware of any dangers which may lurk in the beautiful plant.

*Danger and delight grow on one stalk.*—JOHN LYLY.

# A Selected Bibliography

This list does not include all the books consulted or quoted from but only those of particular relevance which might be available to the general reader through book stores or libraries.

Arnold, Harry L. *Poisonous Plants of Hawaii.* Honolulu: Tongg Publishing Company, 1944.

Bailey, L. H. *Manual of Cultivated Plants.* Revised edition. New York: The Macmillan Company, 1964.

*Bancke's Herbal* (1525). Edited by S. V. Larkey and Thomas Pyles. New York: New York Botanical Garden, 1941.

Coats, Alice M. *Flowers and Their Histories.* London: Pitman Publishing Corporation, 1956.

Culpeper, Nicholas. *Complete Herbal.* London: W. Foulsham & Company, Ltd., No date. (A modern condensation of the original.)

Dioscorides. *The Greek Herbal of Dioscorides.* Edited by Robert T. Gunther. New York: Hafner Publishing Company, Inc., 1959.

Fernald, Merritt Lyndon, and Alfred Charles Kinsey. *Edible Wild Plants of Eastern North America.* Revised by Reed C. Rollins. New York: Harper & Brothers Publishers, 1958.

Freeman, Margaret B. *Herbs for the Mediaeval Household.* New York: The Metropolitan Museum of Art, 1943.

Gerard, John. *Herball. The Essence Thereof Distilled by Marcus Woodward.* London: Spring Books, 1927. (The rare complete edition is dated 1636.)

Gibbons, Euell. *Stalking the Wild Asparagus.* New York: David McKay Company, Inc., 1962.

Grieve, Mrs. M., and Mrs. C. F. Leyel. *A Modern Herbal.* Two volumes. New York: Harcourt, Brace & Company, 1931.

Grigson, Geoffrey. *The Englishman's Flora.* London: Phoenix House, Ltd., 1955.

Harshberger, John W. *Text-Book of Pastoral and Agricultural Botany.* Philadelphia: P. Blakiston's Sons & Company, 1920.

Jacob, Dorothy. *A Witch's Guide to Gardening.* New York: Taplinger Publishing Company, Inc., 1965.

Kingsbury, John M. *Deadly Harvest. A Guide to Common Poisonous Plants.* New York: Holt, Rinehart & Winston, 1965.

Kingsbury, John M. *Poisonous Plants of the United States and Canada.* New York: Prentice-Hall, Inc., 1964.

Kreig, Margaret B. *Green Medicine. The Search for Plants That Heal.* New York: Rand McNally & Company, 1964.

Krutch, Joseph Wood. *Herbal.* New York: G. P. Putnam's Sons, 1965.

Lehner, Ernst and Johanna. *Folklore and Odysseys of Food and Medicinal Plants.* New York: Tudor Publishing Company, 1962.

Lehner, Ernst and Johanna. *Folklore and Symbolism of Flowers, Plants and Trees.* New York: Tudor Publishing Company, 1960.

Leyel, Mrs. C. F. *Elixirs of Life.* London: Faber & Faber Ltd., 1948.

Leyel, Mrs. C. F. *The Magic of Herbs. A Modern Book of Secrets.* New York: Harcourt, Brace & Company, 1926.

Muenscher, Walter Conrad, and Myron Arthur Rice. *Garden Spice and Wild Pot-Herbs.* Ithaca: Cornell University Press, 1955.

Muenscher, Walter Conrad. *Poisonous Plants of the United States.* Revised edition. New York: The Macmillan Company, 1964.

Nicander. *The Poems and Poetical Fragments.* Edited with a translation and note by A. S. F. Gow and A. F. Scholfield. New York: Cambridge University Press, 1953. (The fragments quoted in verse are adaptations by Hubert Creekmore.)

Pammel, L. H. *A Manual of Poisonous Plants.* Iowa City: The Torch Press, 1911.

Pliny. *Natural History.* Translated by W. H. S. Jones. Ten volumes. Loeb Classical Library. Cambridge: Harvard University Press and William Heinemann, Ltd. (Separate volumes issued on various dates.)

*Pseudo-Apuleius.* See T. O. Cockayne: *Leechdoms, Wortcunning and Starcraft of Early England.* 1864. (A recent reprint of this work appeared a few years ago, but I have not seen a copy.)

Quelch, Mary Thorne. *Herbs and How to Know Them.* London: Faber & Faber Ltd., 1946.

Schenk, Gustav. *The Book of Poisons.* Translated from the German by Michael Bullock. New York: Rinehart & Company, Inc., 1955.

Smith, Alexander H. *The Mushroom Hunter's Field Guide*. Ann Arbor: The University of Michigan Press, 1958. (A new revised edition has just been issued.)

Steyn, Douw G. *The Toxicology of Plants in South Africa*. Johannesburg: Central News Agency, Ltd. 1943.

Theophrastus. *Enquiry Into Plants*. Translated by Sir Arthur Hart. Two volumes. Loeb Classical Library. Cambridge: Harvard University Press and London: William Heinemann Ltd., 1916.

Thorwald, Jürgen. *The Century of the Detective*. Translated from the German by Richard and Clara Winston. A Helen and Kurt Wolff Book. New York: Harcourt, Brace and World, Inc., 1965. (The long section on analysis of vegetable poisons is of special interest.)

Walker, Winifred. *All the Plants of the Bible*. New York: Harper & Brothers Publishers, 1957.